LIFE OR DEATH:
Ethics and Options

LIFE OR DEATH:
ETHICS AND OPTIONS

EDWARD SHILS, NORMAN ST.JOHN–STEVAS,

PAUL RAMSEY, P. B. MEDAWAR,

HENRY K. BEECHER, ABRAHAM KAPLAN

Introduction by Daniel H. Labby

REED COLLEGE
Portland, Oregon
UNIVERSITY OF WASHINGTON PRESS
Seattle and London

174.2
L 626

Acknowledgment

THE papers included in this volume were presented at a symposium on *The Sanctity of Life* held March 11–12, 1966, at Reed College, Portland, Oregon, under the sponsorship of Bess Kaiser Hospital and Reed College.

Contents

Introduction

THERE is little difficulty recalling the details of the birth of this first symposium in the Sanctity of Life series. The planning committee had wrestled for some weeks with a wide variety of universal social problems, but when the idea of "The Sanctity of Life" was first presented, its appeal was sensed unanimously. At the moment an unpopular war was threatening to escalate insanely, and the use of nuclear power in war was a world-wide anxiety. The problems of racism and rioting were again aflame, the wounds of the thalidomide tragedy were still unhealed, and contraception and abortion were troublesome moral dilemmas. There could be no more opportune topic for a conference than one that would explore the ethics and options controlling the powers of life and death.

Is life more, or less valuable today, than at any moment in

DANIEL H. LABBY

the recorded history of man? Could one identify the forces in society that determine how valuable one man holds the life of another? Do adequate guidelines exist in law, theology, or in the liberal arts? Are the biomedical sciences, dedicated to preserving health and prolonging life, taking undue liberties in the guise of improving man's condition? The conference planning committee approached the selection of participants with these questions uppermost. In the scientific area some of the numerous threats to life were easily identified: contraception, abortion, eugenics, euthanasia, drug testing, and human experimentation. The biologists and medical scientist were absolutely essential. In view of the spectacular powers of science, the parallel questions of morality in the employment of these powers might be raised first. Has the growth of moral thought been consistent with the explosion of scientific knowledge? S. E. Stumpf [1] claims that through its history, medicine has shown sensitivity to the moral dimension of its practices: ". . . the momentum of modern medicine has provoked a philosophical dialogue forcing all the parties to it to consider certain questions that not too long ago seemed more clear and settled: those questions concerning the value of human life, the basis of human dignity, the goal of human existence and the corollary duties of medicine to be governed by these assumptions."

But the scientists could not be allowed to have the picnic all to themselves; they should be exposed to counterpoint from enlightened nonscientists. Canon Bentley [2] had specified that "science certainly has a big part to play in ethics because every ethical decision has to be made on the basis of facts. But the actual decision involves something that science cannot supply, concerned as it is with the measureable, and not with values." In other words, values lie beyond the domain of science.

Certainly law would be one discipline indispensable to the conference. It is the prime and stable principle of continuity in our society and would be the first specific and enforceable limitation science might encounter. Has the increased pace of social change, as a result of the innovations of science, brought flexibility to these boundaries and to interpretations of law?

[1] S. E. Stumpf, "Some Moral Dimensions of Medicine," *Annals of Internal Medicine*, LXIV (February, 1966), 460.
[2] G. E. W. Wolstenholme and Maeve O'Connor (ed.), *Ethics in Medical Progress: With Special Reference to Transplantation* (Ciba Foundation Symposium; Boston: Little, Brown, 1966).

The question must be internalized, since law and social change function reciprocally (though the law changes with glacial slowness); both may impose restrictions on science. René Dubos [3] has commented on this point: "In reality . . . the greatest difficulty in the achievement of health in the modern world will not come from learning more things and learning to handle a little better what we know but rather from all sorts of social limitations that would prevent us from applying the knowledge that we have. These social limitations cannot help bringing to the medical community extremely difficult problems of conscience in the near future."

The power of science and the limitations of the law and social order suggest that the privacy and the rights of the individual might be invaded. In light of contemporary moral concerns, an observer of man's social institutions and behavior—a sociologist—should be invited to comment on the relevance of this to the sanctity of life. Likewise, religion and philosophy could scarcely be overlooked. There is such uncertainty about the force of religious belief in face of modern scientific inquiry that one might reasonably ask what the role of religious principles will be in guiding human behavior.

Since the entire discourse was well within the domain of philosophy, at least in its traditional function of looking at the problems of man, one of the most difficult tasks in the conference was assigned a philosopher: that of commenting at the end of the discussions in the hope that a final common path

[3] "The Great Issues of Conscience in Modern Medicine," Dartmouth Convocation (September, 1960).

might be found, of reason, of arbitration (if necessary), and at least of common sense, if not pure logic. "There is no system of philosophy to spin out," says Donald Kalish, chairman of the Department of Philosophy at the University of California at Los Angeles. "There are no ethical truths, there are just clarifications of particular ethical problems." Implied in our choice was a decision on the philosophic issue of whether life is worth while at all, and as stated in a recent *Time* essay: "Philosophy, traditionally, has been nothing less than the attempt to ask and answer, in a formal and disciplined way, the great questions of life that ordinary men might put to themselves in reflective moments." [4] This is essentially what the conference set out to do.

There is no limit to the span and reach of ethical discourse under the general umbrella of the Sanctity of Life. One might explore endlessly the morality of killing in war and include the question of conscientious objection. Indeed, the assignment of guilt and innocence many years after war still seems to hold the world's attention. Capital punishment and the right to take a life, planned genetics and the control of the quality of life—these and many more issues could keep us at our deliberations endlessly. The heart of the matter seemed to be to plan a conference, as the first of a series, with a confrontation between scientists and nonscientists.

One hazard was apparent in so doing: that the two cultures of C. P. Snow, the two worlds of the literary and the scien-

[4] "What (If Anything) to Expect from Today's Philosophers," *Time* (January 7, 1966), p. 24.

tific, might start turning slowly against each other once again. There was even risk that effective communication might not be established between scientists and nonscientists in areas of mutual concern and dilemma. The traditional world of literature and the humanities has had too little voice in the ever-expanding world of the scientist. An intellectual standoffishness seems to have developed with the formation of one of those impassable lines such as existed in Victorian England between tradesmen and gentlemen. A distant debt was mutually acknowledged; each offered the other vague, respectful and grudging recognition (since neither could ignore the other), though with little affection. This is mindful of the elegant epitaph:

> Here lies the body of Eliza
> She was a wonderful cook, a fine mother
> And saved my money.
> But I never learned to like her.

Science was unsavory to the liberal arts because it inevitably "dehumanized man" and insisted that the arts meet its unreasonable demands. Historically, science developed in response to human spiritual desire to understand the universe, man's relation to it, and the order and beauty in nature. From all of this came the know-how to build temples, cathedrals, and theaters, and to make calculations of astronomical change for religious observance.

The origin of the humanities was hardly less utilitarian. The liberal arts were born at least twenty-four hundred years ago in Athens, and the knowledge then passed to the Latin educators, the monks during the Dark Ages, and then to the schoolmasters of the Renaissance, who handed it on to modern Europe and America. The total effect of this long tradition in learning was to train free men to exercise their proper function in society by developing skills in the art of speech and persuasion, "an exact knowledge of the value of words and an understanding of the laws of thought and the rules of logic." The whole idea of education has always been the use of words and the handling of ideas clearly, precisely, and even elegantly. The humanities and the sciences alike are useful in practical ways; both are creative; both are intellectually and spiritually satisfying, and they can illuminate each other.

The power of science has been gathering since the Industrial Revolution and now is of a magnitude never before witnessed on Earth. Serious questions arise as moral imperatives: "For what purpose and to what end shall power be employed?" Scientific information has accumulated at such a rate that wisdom may never be able to keep pace. Dr. Roger Revelle, chairman of the United States National Committee for the International Biological Program, has said, "In our times of unprecedented change biologists are aware of the rapidly growing ability of their fellow human beings to alter the face of the earth through technology. But they are equally aware that these alterations can bring about far spreading and often destructive changes in the web of life that is stretched so thinly over the surface of our planet. Our technology has outspaced our understanding, our cleverness has grown faster than our wisdom." To seek wisdom out of cleverness was a major commitment for all participants in the conference. It was hoped that through this search a base for the sanctity of life might be provided.

As a sociologist, Professor Edward Shils began with a most disarming dissection by suggesting that "the inviolability of human life seems to be so self-evident that it might appear pointless to inquire into it," and with a classic reference to Christian teaching, suggesting that human life is especially sacred and inviolate because God has created man. According to Professor Shils, man's superior qualities are further characterized by the assignment of a destiny, a sense of participation in the nature of the universe, and the possession of biological vitality and soul (or mind). But the experience of Nazi destruction, the fading of Christian belief, and the new confidence in our biomedical sciences suggest that both destructive and salvaging forces can work side by side as man pursues his destiny. The essential questions to Shils are "whether life is sacred," and "how far morality permits and how far the law should allow us to intervene into reproduction, the course of life, and the constitution of individuality and privacy." Professor Shils extensively explores the Christian view of man, interference with the genetic determinates of life, and scientific modifications of personality. His range is wide, and his sense of anticipation nothing short of clairvoyant. His credo is that "if life were not viewed and experienced as sacred, then nothing else would be sacred." The enormous intellectual area encompassed by this figure receives both broad and deep treatment. It is highly recommended that the reader actually begin the deliberations of the conference at the beginning—with Professor Shils's contribution.

"Law both reflects and preserves the moral consensus of society," Norman St. John–Stevas, barrister and member of Parliament, offers in opening his argument. He quickly qualifies the way this operates, however, in a kind of rubric that "not all of the moral consensus will be enforced by law, although the law will always take account of it," and "the moral consensus is not given for all time," and "the law cannot guarantee ultimate rightness." But in exploring the thrust of the law he hastens to point out that "Concepts which direct the dynamism of the common law include those of fairness, reasonableness, and observance of the rules of natural justice," and suggests that one concept presumed by every branch of law (especially in criminal law) is that of the sanctity of life. Professor Shils and Mr. St. John–Stevas move very close to each other at this point. "Medieval law was dominated by the idea of natural law," says St. John–Stevas, "our own, by the assumption of the existence of human rights. This is reinforced by modern man's psychological awareness of his own uniqueness. The law assumes the value of human life as a fact: it does not seek to explain it"—a somewhat rhetorical echo to Professor Shils's question and answer, "Is human life really sacred?"—"Self-evidently!" To both, the proposition is a guiding principle.

After identifying the concept of the sanctity of life as basic to law, Mr. St. John–Stevas occupies himself principally with the problem of abortion and to a lesser extent with those of euthanasia, suicide, and capital punishment. His contention that man is in danger of being dehumanized and that salvation may be based on the Christian doctrine, that "man is not absolute master of his own fate, but holds his life and body in trust for other purposes," suggests that these concepts "preserve his humanity by erecting barriers beyond which technology cannot pass." Man "could do worse than be guided by the wisdom of the common law, with its centuries-old recognition of man's dignity and freedom," a point of view broadly explored at the conference and in his book, *The Right to Life*.

By the good fortune that occasionally comes to conference planning, Professor Paul Ramsey's theological discourse follows closely the interpretations of Christian concept by Mr. St. John–Stevas. Ramsey examines, in pinpoint detail, considerations of the moment when germinating life becomes human, before staking out abortion as a crime. He reviews with thoroughness the ancient concepts of animation, traducianism, and creationism, though in honest confession he says, "having begun with all these distinctions and theories about when germinating life has become human, it is now necessary for me to say that from an authentic religious point of view none of them matters very much." In support of his charge of abortion as a crime, his elaborate reinforcement for the Christian beliefs of St. John–Stevas and his distinctions are elegant: "I suggest that a strong case can be made for

every effort to revitalize a religious understanding of the
integrity and sanctity of life, for unfolding from this at the
outmost limits the distinction between direct killing and allowing to die and the distinction between intending to kill and
intending to incapacitate the fetus to save the mother's life,
and for retaining in the order of ethical justification the prohibition of the direct killing of nascent life." It is these moral
pressures, he believes, that we must keep upon ourselves
"where a proper regard for life threatens to be dissolved."

At this midpoint in the conference, intellectual collisions
were becoming obvious: Professor Shils had spoken of "the
fading of Christian belief," but both Professor Ramsey and
Mr. St. John–Stevas reaffirmed their faith in the Christian
doctrine, one through an historical and liturgical perspective
of theology, and the other claiming Christianity as the broad
base for the humane considerations of law. Professor Shils had
referred to the Nazi destruction and the dropping of two
nuclear bombs (despite centuries of church doctrine) as unprecedented horrors, while affirming confidence in the biomedical sciences. "Nonetheless, the occurrence of war, murder, capital punishment, torture, and indifference to human
suffering no more invalidates the hypothesis of the widespread affirmation of the sanctity of life than the fact of suicide annuls the proposition of the near universality of the
individual's appreciation of his own vitality and its continuance"; and "As regards the sanctity of life itself, the biological-
technological innovations we have been considering do not
diminish life, they improve it. They do not constrict it, rather

they enlarge it as far as individual human beings are concerned."

It came as no surprise that the first scientist to speak, Sir Peter Medawar, did not deny "that the advances of science may sometimes have consequences that endanger, if not life itself, then the quality of life or our self-respect as human beings (for it is in this wider sense that I think 'sanctity' should be construed)." In spite of the reference to mass murder and nuclear bombs, however, Dr. Medawar chose to feel that "The mischief . . . grows just as often out of trying to do good . . . as out of actions intended to be destructive." "There must be very few wicked scientists. There are, however, plenty of wicked philosophers, wicked priests, and wicked politicians." He contended that evils from science stem from a lack of foresight in visualizing the "distant consequences of scientific innovation." One may offer a reasonable rebuttal: for "foresight" should we read "insight"? Might a more insightful examination of the moral limitations of applied science, a more meditative and deliberate effort to anticipate the consequences (though slowing the momentum of discovery) deviate or stop the awesome rush to the abyss? There are those proponents of the humanities who feel the pace of science to be giddy and unstable and would prescribe large doses of moral imperatives. Are not the humanities, in Robert Graves's terms, "no more than the steadying tail of the technological kite now being carried up far out of sight on an endless, weightless irrefragable string?" [5]

[5] Robert Graves, "A Poet's Investigation of Science" (Arthur D. Little Lecture), *Saturday Review* (December 7, 1963).

Dr. Medawar's argument takes us off in another direction and into an area of greater predictability: human genetics and eugenics. He cannot avoid the arguments over the disposal of qualitatively poor and monstrous genetic material, and the problem of abortion, but he does not spare us his firm belief in the morality of it all. His fine wordcraft should be saved annotation and be read for its own flavor. With D. H. Lawrence, he believes in "a certain natural sense of the fitness of things, a feeling that is shared by most kind and reasonable people even if we cannot define it in philosophically defensible or legally accountable terms." Global considerations are suddenly scaled down on a person-to-person basis, to the ultimate unit of the mother science, medicine; to doctor and patient, to the scientist who would apply his knowledge and to the patient who would receive it for his betterment. Should world-wide probabilities of risk (the statistical morality) influence the scientist vis-à-vis one patient, or should the unique gains and losses of the moment in a single patient (the individual morality) be his only concern? Dr. Thomas E. Starzl believes that the physician proceeds to discharge his responsibility without regard for the conceivably broader issue of whether treatment is justifiable on social grounds.

His reasons may include pride, altruism, compassion, curiosity, a spirit of competition, even avarice, or a combination of all these things. Whatever the motives, the reflexes that follow are sure, and respond similarly to the needs of the productive members of the community, the insane and feeble minded, children with incurable birth defects, condemned criminals, or even soldiers who, moments before, were members of a hostile army.

The foregoing viewpoint is a narrow one but there is no reason to believe that it should be abandoned in the face of advancing technocracy. It has shielded the ill from the caprices of the moral judgements of other men through centuries of evolving philosophical, religious, and legal doctrines. It has placed the concept of the sanctity of human life on a practical foundation, since the responsibility of one person for another could not be more clearly defined than through the doctor-patient relationship, irrespective of the reasons for the contract entered into between the two involved parties.[6]

Starzl's statement prepares us well for Dr. Henry K. Beecher's discussion of the ethical problems arising in experimentation on man. Beecher would add one further qualification to our considerations of the moral dilemma: "We are to be concerned here only with experimentation in one patient, not at all for his specific benefit, but, hopefully, for the benefit of patients in general." Though a doctor may experiment while treating the patient, this is interpreted in the patient's mind as therapy. The human experimental subject, however, is manipulated; and in Dr. Beecher's mind this opens the possibility for breaches of ethical conduct in experimentation. To protect the patient and safeguard the morality, Dr. Beecher would insist that there be "informed consent," and "an informed, intelligent, skillful, compassionate, responsible investigator." Stumpf has seen this as a problem combining morality and technological momentum. After con-

---

[6] "The Changing Mores of Biomedical Research: A Colloquium on Ethical Dilemmas from Medical Advances," *Annals of Internal Medicine*, LXVII, Supplement 7 (September, 1967).

siderable thought as to whether the investigators were justified in using human subjects for such things as elective experimental surgery and the injection of live cancer cells, he concluded that, rather than limiting the problem to the actions of the unqualified, it was to him "a condition virtually inherent in clinical investigations where human beings are used as subjects." But, to preserve moral stringency, he asks whether it is wise "to limit the use of human subjects to those cases where informed consent was obtained and does consent solve the problem?" [7] Does consent carry far too great a burden, can consent transform something intrinsically wrong into a right? Dr. Beecher soundly presents the whole flavor of the question of valid consent by an exploration of the ingredients in "full knowledge of risk," and offers an intriguing underlining to the ethical dilemmas of human experimentation. Dr. Beecher finally considers the "conscience and responsibility of the investigator," a phrase not yet heard in the conference. To close the circle of argument, we might use the suggestion of C. P. Snow, who believes that "conscience" might be a substitute for "moral nature." [8]

The final remarks by Professor Kaplan were awaited with enormous anticipation. The arguments had been so far-ranging and complex that it was thought impossible to offer an adequate and deserving summary, but this is a final delight left to the delectation of the reader. It is brilliant, thoughtful, penetrating, and graceful. The flavor of Kaplan's presenta-

[7] Stumpf, "Some Moral Dimensions of Medicine," p. 460.
[8] "Great Issues of Conscience in Modern Medicine."

tion was heightened by the introduction of him, which quoted from his book, *American Ethics and Public Policy.* In the introduction to this volume, Kaplan says of himself: "I [am] by training a positivist, by inclination a pragmatist, in temperament a mystic, in practice a Democrat; my faith Jewish, educated by the Catholics, an habitual protestant; born in Europe, raised in the Midwest, hardened in the East, and softened once more in California." Professor Kaplan's summing up is a remarkable extemporaneous document, all the more remarkable considering the circumstances of fatigue and strain at the end of a long and difficult day. His statement is a final explosion of gentle strength and humor, of incisiveness and perception, of beauty and immense satisfaction.[9]

Portland, Oregon
October, 1967

[9] Subsequently three of the papers were published in slightly altered forms: Edward Shils's essay appeared in *Encounter* (January, 1967); "Law and the Sanctity of Life" by Norman St. John–Stevas appeared in the *Dublin Review* (Summer, 1966); under the title, "Science and the Sanctity of Life," P. B. Medawar's essay appeared in *Encounter* (December, 1966).

THE SANCTITY OF LIFE
Volume I

The Sanctity of Life

To PERSONS who are not murderers, concentration camp administrators, or dreamers of sadistic fantasies, the inviolability of human life seems to be so self-evident that it might appear pointless to inquire into it. To inquire into it is embarrassing as well because, once raised, the question seems to commit us to beliefs we do not wish to espouse and to confront us with contradictions which seem to deny what is self-evident. Yet because of a conjunction of circumstances, it is worth while to initiate such an inquiry.

One of these circumstances is the decline of Christian belief about the place of man in the divine scheme and the consequent diminution of its force as a criterion in the judgment of the worth and permissibility of human actions. As long as it was believed that man was created by God in His own image and had been assigned a cosmic destiny by Him, it seemed

EDWARD SHILS

evident that man's life was a sacred entity. It was sacred in the sense that it partook of the very nature of the universe; for that reason man's biological vitality and his soul (or mind) were not to be subjected to the transforming manipulations of other men. The cognitive content of Christian doctrine, and above all the grandiose Christian symbolization of man's origin and destiny, have now lost much of their appeal. Large sections of contemporary Western societies, particularly the highly educated, do not believe in divine creation. They do not, by and large, believe in the immortality of the soul. They probably do not believe in a soul at all. The idea of redemption beyond this life is a phantasm as far as they are concerned. If there is no God, no divine creation, no immortality of the soul, no redemption, why should man's life be regarded with any more reverence than we regard the lives of wild and

3

domestic animals which we hunt or breed and eat, or pets which we cherish? After the first pleasures of iconoclasm, serious agnostics, concerned about an ultimate ground of moral judgment and a basis for moral discipline, vaguely sense a void left behind by the rejection of an unacceptable divinity. They do not know how, but they think that the void must be filled.

Another of the epochal circumstances which have caused us to raise the questions discussed in this paper is the advancement of the life sciences and the technological possibilities based on them. Biological knowledge has been in the process of growth for three centuries, but in recent decades its progress has become much more fundamental. (The advance is to some extent a function of the great improvement in instrumental technology, e.g., the electronic microscope.) Surgery is also old, but it has become vastly more daring in its undertakings and proficient in its accomplishments in recent decades. The life sciences seem on the verge of an efflorescence like that through which the physical sciences passed during the first half of the present century. They are beginning to attract talents of a quality—and in large numbers—such as physics attracted in its recent very great period. As a result, life scientists, physicians, and surgeons are beginning to acquire unprecedented knowledge and capacities to intervene purposefully and effectively in the course of the life of individuals and in the reproduction of generations.

Alongside these heightened powers of observation of the human organism and intervention into its vital processes, the powers of observing—of seeing and hearing—and of reaching into the social behavior of human beings, have increased correspondingly. These latter developments are in part functions of technological improvements. In part they are also functions of the "cognitive explosion," of greater curiosity, greater sympathy, and more scientific detachment, and an aspiration for a more far-reaching and more deeply penetrating surveillance and control. The coincidence of the cognitive explosion, the larger size of the corporate bodies into which so much of modern society is organized, and the greater complexity of the total societies seems to call for more knowledge and more control. Once again the potentialities of technology and the power of those who are its masters give rise to an almost shapeless apprehension.

We live also in an epoch in which one of the most famous countries, Germany, not particularly dechristianized as compared with the other countries of the modern world, participated in the deliberate murder of numerous millions of persons of alien ethnic stocks. Mankind was accustomed to the destruction of lives by war, and to murder by individuals acting out of powerfully passionate and transient impulses. The Nazi destruction was, however, so unprecedented in its scale, organization, persistence, and "rationality" that many sensitive persons have now come to feel that we live unsteadily and unceasingly suspended over an abyss of unlimited murderousness. Another memorial of this epoch is the dropping of the two nuclear bombs at the end of World War II. Each of these destroyed more human lives than any single and separate action performed by a small number of men had ever done before. The nuclear weapons were made possible by the scientific research performed in the present century by some of the greatest minds of human history.

Christian belief has faded, and the plausible confidence of the biomedical sciences has grown. We have become more aware of the destructive capacities of sadism served by large-scale organization—which was occasionally justified by the invocation of pseudo-scientific genetic doctrines and which was attended by some alleged medical experiments—and of the fact that genuinely outstanding scientific genius served, or was utilized for, military purposes in the atomic bomb. All these developments have raised a fundamental question. How is the human race as we have known it, with all its deficiencies, to be protected from the murderous and manipulative wickedness of some of its members and from the passionate curiosity and the scientific and technological genius of others? Each of these major factors working alone would have raised questions about the grounds on which one man's life or individuality may be interfered with, changed, or discontinued, and the factors which might extend or restrict such acts of intervention. Their confluence renders it desirable to consider the whole problem more closely. This is why we ask the questions as to whether life is sacred, and as to how far morality permits and how far the law should allow us to intervene into reproduction, the course of life, and the constitution of individuality and privacy.

Despite the diminution of theological belief among the educated, many persons, including the educated, experience a sense of abhorrence in the face of the new or prospective capacities of geneticists, neurosurgeons, pharmacologists, psychiatrists, psychologists, and electronics engineers to intervene into what has hitherto been regarded largely as given by man's ancestry and his "natural" cognitive and moral powers. The loosening of the hold of ancestry, the circumvention of normal sexual intercourse as a precondition of procreation, the modification of memory, temperament, and sensory experience, all produce an effect of shock in many persons—and it is not just the shock of surprise in the presence of novelty. It is closer to deep abhorrence or revulsion. We see it in the struggles of courts and lawyers to cope with these new facts of human existence. We see it in the responses of those who still accept the Christian views of man, and we see it among the agnostic humanists who think that their view of the world is entirely secular and utilitarian. But the formulation of an intellectually coherent, rationally acceptable justification of the sense of abhorrence seems to present difficulties.

Why do so many persons experience this vague and sometimes passionate revulsion at the thought of a deliberate modification of the genetic determinants of the life of a human being, or of the modification of the personality by a neurosurgical operation, or of the observation and recording of a conversation which is believed by the participants to be held

7

tistically the most frequent nor a product of indoctrination, although both play a part in forming its content and maintaining it. Much of this conception of the "normal" or the "natural" centers on heterosexuality, lineage ties, and the integrity of the human organism and its memory.

Such developments as the transplantation of organs, the implantation of substitute organs made from inorganic materials, the instigation and control of human reproductive processes independently of sexual intercourse (artificial inovulation and insemination), the prospective modification of genetic constitution, the modification of personality qualities by prefrontal lobotomy, the termination of pregnancy by abortion, electrical-shock therapy, the transformation of memory by electronic devices or chemical substances, the pharmaceutical transformation of the senses and the imagination, generate in different ways among many persons of all sorts and conditions some apprehension about the dangers of deviation from the "normal" and the "natural" which are obscurely intimated by these increased powers. These apprehensions are not just vestiges of archaic theological beliefs; they are not just "learned cultural responses." They are also direct responses to sacrilege.

Abhorrence and apprehension are accentuated by the fact that the very possibilities of contrived intervention are greeted by numerous persons with great enthusiasm. Those who are put off by these new possibilities, who shudder at the sight or thought of this new Promethean aspiration to do things which lay hitherto beyond human powers, are further alarmed by the frivolity of the enthusiasts, who show no sign of concern for the moral overtones of the possibilities and alternatives which they praise. The anxiety about the moral status of these interventions is aggravated by the affront to a conventional outlook, and this renders unlikely a calm consideration of the moral and metaphysical issues which are involved. It is thus more difficult to think about the institutional controls that could restrict the use of the new techniques of intervention for diabolical purposes, and to clarify moral standards and develop legal rules and institutions adequate to deal with new conceptions of criteria of death, parenthood, and so forth.

The unqualified enthusiasm of the proponents and prophets of "contrived intervention" only further disturbs and alarms those who would have misgivings enough about the new possibilities without having to confront the enthusiasts. It must nonetheless be acknowledged that the enthusiasts stand in a great tradition. The improvement of the physical quality of life, the promotion of a life without pain or unhappiness, the improvement in human powers and the pleasure in the exercise of the powers of knowing and constructing—prizing these accomplishments is part of our most valuable traditions. Yet among the motives of the enthusiasts there are probably also some which are less worthy, such as aspirations to omnipotence, and desires to manipulate the individuality and to intrude on the privacy of human beings and therewith to enjoy the experience of degrading them.

These latter motives, to the extent that they are thought

to exist, give Prometheanism a bad name. It should be remembered, however, that Prometheus was a benefactor of the human race who suffered because he sought to displace the gods by diffusing their powers among men. Those who stand uneasily apart from the interventions which are being made possible by recent biomedical and technological advances might not believe that there are certain kinds of knowledge which belong only to God; they are not, however, confident about the wisdom or the self-restraint of men in dealing with the sanctity of life and in respecting the "natural" or the "normal" in which that sacredness is incorporated, when technical possibilities of infringing on it become more easily available. After all, even under technologically far more rudimentary conditions, murder and cruelty for its own sake have found many practitioners.

The chief feature of the protoreligious, "natural metaphysic" is the affirmation that life *is* sacred. It is believed to be sacred not because it is a manifestation of a transcendent creator from whom life comes: It is believed to be sacred because it is life. The idea of sacredness is generated by the primordial experience of being alive, of experiencing the elemental sensation of vitality and the elemental fear of its extinction. Man stands in awe before his own vitality, the vitality of his lineage and of his species. The sense of awe is the attribution and therefore the acknowledgment of sanctity. All else which man feels to be sacred derives its sanctity because it controls or embodies that sacred vitality of the individual, the lineage, and the species.

The fear of the extinction of vitality, of one's own organism, of the species, and of one's own lineage, testifies to the primordial attachment to the elemental fact of vitality. What is at work here is not merely the attachment of the individual human organism, which experiences and appreciates its own vitality. It is also an appreciation of the continuity of the vitality of one's own breed and progeny, unborn and unknown, the vitality of the territorial and civil community of which one is a member and the vitality of the species. Within this context, these are thought to be "normal" or "natural" modes of embodiment of the vital. When we speak of the sanctity of life, it is of the sanctity of these "normal" forms of life that we speak.

To say that the idea of the sacred is at bottom the appreciation of vitality requires some explanation, because it seems to be so contradictory to the usual idea which asserts that the sacred lies outside and beyond both the individual organic and the collective carriers of vitality. It is often asserted that these are sacred because they are infused with or touched by or generated by transcendent sacred powers. My own view is that the transcendent sacred is a construction which the human mind itself has created to account for and to place in a necessary order the primordial experience—and vicissitudes —of the actual embodiment of vitality to which it attributes sacredness. In this process of construction, many objects and abstract entities come to have sacredness imputed to them; they become transcendent bearers and sources of sacredness.

We value the transcendent sacred because we impute to it the powers which are thought to have generated human vitality, and which maintain, enhance, and protect it. The ultimate laws that govern human vitality and its manifestations—whether they be the laws of the physical and organic universe disclosed by scientific research, whether they be the properties of divinity disclosed by revelation, the study of sacred books, and theological analysis, or whether they be the laws of society disclosed and promulgated by research, reason, and authority—possess their property of sanctity because they are believed to govern, underlie, account for, guide, and control human vitality. These symbolic constructions possess sanctity, or rather have it attributed to them, because they explain why *life*—and the universe which is its frame and ground, and society which enfolds and contains it —exists and because they control its movement, whether they do so through the laws of the universe of physical and organic nature or in the form of the laws of society in general or of a particular society.

If man did not prize his own vitality, the sacred and its vast symbolic elaboration into cosmogonies and theologies would not exist. The sacred and its symbolic proliferation have been created and have held dominion over so many human beings through much of the course of history because of the need to place in an order of power and justice the vicissitudes of human vitality. If life were not viewed and experienced as sacred, then nothing else would be sacred. This is true of societies which are regarded as increasingly secular as well as of those which for their entire history have lived with a powerful admixture of traditional religious belief and practice.

If human beings attribute sacredness to human life, why do so many human beings destroy life and condone its destruction? Why are they so apparently indifferent to the lives of their fellow men? Why are some men actively destructive of the lives of their fellow men?

Until well into modern times, rulers in most parts of the world, and even now in many, have been and are largely indifferent to the vital condition of their subjects and countrymen. Generals have often thrown away the lives of large numbers of their soldiers. Churches and states have persecuted and destroyed lives. Governmental authorities have destroyed those who have, in fact or symbolically, endangered the political and social order.

Often those who deny the sanctity of particular individual lives do so on behalf of institutions which they themselves regard as sacred. Moreover, the incumbents of the institutional roles to which sacredness is attributed frequently regard their own sanctity as having overriding rights vis-à-vis other claimants to sanctity. States and churches, which regard themselves as possessing sanctity, do not find it difficult to disregard or deny the sanctity of the lives of particular individuals, at the same time believing themselves still com-

15

mitted to the sanctity of life as such, and even more to the sanctity of their own institutions.

But it is not just the custodians of collective sanctity who infringe on the sanctity of individual lives. Murders by private citizens are common to say the least; multitudes are killed inadvertently by careless or incompetent automobile drivers; human lives are abbreviated by man-made pollution of the air. Violent hatred and sheer indifference show that the sense of the sanctity of life is often faint and feeble. The sense of the sanctity of individual life is not in exclusive possession of the field of forces which control human life. It is under perpetual pressure from sacrilegious and destructive dispositions and from its own tendency to shrivel into insensitivity or indifference.

Nonetheless, the occurrence of war, murder, capital punishment, torture, and indifference to human suffering no more invalidates the hypothesis of the widespread affirmation of the sanctity of life than the fact of suicide annuls the proposition of the near universality of the individual's appreciation of his own vitality and its continuance. The real problem is how to explain the coexistence of these several contradictory tendencies.

Like the powers of reason and imagination, sensitivity to the sacred is unequally distributed among the members of any given society. It is also intermittent in its operation and of uneven intensity in the extent to which it attributes sacredness to different individuals and collectivities, and to extra-human events. Some lives are regarded as more sacred than other lives. (This is true with respect both to the sanctity of the vitality of the individual and to the various forms and symbols of transcendent powers in which the sacredness of life is objectified.) There is a gradation of "sanctity" moving from the individual outward—first through his kinship and affectional attachments, then local, national, class, ethnic group, and culture, becoming more attenuated and patchier as it reaches into other countries, continents, and races.[1] Just as the personal affections diminish as they radiate outward, so the sense of identity constituted by a sense of shared sanctity also diminishes—although it has far greater radiative capacity than personal affection.

A point of disjunction in the downward curve of attribution of sanctity, a point beyond which the sanctity imputed to human life becomes a matter of indifference, seems to occur where it is thought that primordial or genetic affinity ends or becomes very thin. There is less concern for the lives of those outside the presumptive genetic network of which we regard ourselves as part. Tribe, caste, ethnic group, nationality, and the national state—the boundaries of these groups are the points of disjunction, beyond which human life is less sacred than it is within.

But even within those boundaries, the sanctity of life is

[1] There is also a reverse gradation, with wider collectivities—such as church or state or nation—having the highest concentration of imputed sanctity and the individual and his kinship group having relatively little. Dispositions toward one gradation or the other vary among individuals, and within individuals, over time.

17

subject to infringement. Much destruction of life takes place within primordial groups and in civil communities. Members of families are cruel to each other, and a substantial proportion of all murders occurs within families. Internal peace is the mark of a civil society, but the most civil society experiences the occurrence of murders, beatings, and cruelty in many other forms. There is, in fact, no situation in which the acknowledgment of the sanctity of life is guaranteed.

Indeed, in the very fact of its sanctity lies some part of the danger to which life is exposed. Sanctity calls forth sacrilegious dispositions. The affirmation of vitality arouses an impulse to destroy it. (Conversely, the awareness of these destructive, desecrating impulses calls forth a protective reaffirmation of the sanctity of life, and one which is indeed often fused with destructive impulses of its own—as, for example, in the case of capital punishment for murder and treason.)

Detachment, the absence of a sense of affinity with other human beings, makes their injury and destruction easier— although a total sense of disaffinity exists only at the psychopathological margins. Thus, in most cases of destruction there is probably some element of a sense of affinity, and some sense of the sacredness of life, which is overpowered by fear, hatred, and sacrilegious impulses, and which arouses guilt which is overcome by further acts of sacrilege.

All that I have been saying so far is descriptive. The question still remains: is human life really sacred? I answer that it is, self-evidently. Its sacredness is the most primordial of experiences, and the fact that many human beings act contrarily, or do not apprehend it, does not impugn the sacredness of life. The facts that many people tell lies, and that scientific truths cannot be appreciated except by those who have been trained to appreciate them, do not make scientific propositions any less truthful, nor do they abolish the intrinsic value of scientific truth. The fact that many human beings often act irrationally does not deny the value of reason.

But even if my affirmation is accepted, our problems are still far from solution. The proposition that life is sacred is no more than a guiding principle. The forms of human life that are sacred, however, are so variegated, so often in tension with each other, and so resistant to being placed on a clear-cut scale of degrees of sacredness, that infinitely difficult problems remain in deciding what is permissible or intolerable.

I should like, therefore, to examine some of the major modes of "contrived intervention" in the light of the guiding principle.

At the outset of this stage of the discussion, I should state that, although I am not an enthusiast for "contrived intervention," and am in fact distrustful of those who envisage an entirely new and wholly better humanity in consequence of the development of the life sciences and certain types of biomedical and other technologies, I do not regard the problem, at least as it appears at present, as really very worrying. To begin at the simplest levels, we have always accepted the surgery which excises a diseased and dispensable organ, such as a gall bladder or even a lung. We have always accepted the surgery which replaced a nonfunctioning or diseased part of the body by an artificial substitute, such as a false tooth or an artificial limb. Is the introduction of a plastic aorta qualitatively different from the introduction of a porcelain tooth? Is it more of an infringement or deformation of individuality? Clearly not.

Blood transfusions too have been accepted, even though they go further than the other types of surgery by the introduction of substances from the body of another human being. This would appear to verge on the infringement of individuality. But the fact is that the introduction of blood or a kidney from another human being, living or dead, works—to the extent that it works at all—only if the organism asserts its systemic coherence and integrates the foreign element into itself. A kidney and blood are alien substances, but the organism remains an organism and assimilates them into its systemic biological individuality. Hence, I do not think that the vitality of the individual human organism is infringed by such surgical interventions. The organism as a whole retains its coherence and continuity, and its vitality is in fact extended and reinvigorated. Surgical technology as it is working today, or is likely to work in the future, does not infringe on the sanctity of life. Rather the opposite: It affirms the sanctity of life by extending and enhancing vitality, and it offers no affront to moral individuality. It raises no moral problems beyond those which medical practice has always had to face.[2]

Since such "reconstructions" are not undertaken without the consent of the patient or the responsible members of his or her family, ethically and logically the situation is the same here as in all medical treatment. The physician is the expert who proposes a course of action, but it is not within his powers—given the traditional pattern of medical belief and

[2] Of course, these technological operations which require extremely scarce skills and resources almost always require decisions with moral overtones as to whether they should be undertaken and, if so, who among the possible beneficiaries should be chosen. And this does place a responsibility for a moral decision on a physician or surgeon, just as the choice of men to be sent out on a dangerous patrol involves an officer in a moral choice as to whose life should be preserved and whose should be endangered or destroyed. The affirmation of the sanctity of life as such does not remove moral dilemmas given the diversity of the forms of life, the existence of other values, and the ineluctable fact of scarcity.

But because medical resources are greater now and demands for medical services are greater still, the moral dilemmas involved have become more explicit and more frequent. The decision that one person rather than another should be allowed to benefit by an "artificial kidney" machine, when there is only one machine and two persons simultaneously in need of treatment, does not raise any question about the sacredness of life as such. It raises questions about whose life is more sacred, and therefore more worthy of preservation. In fact, the terribly painful decisions which must be made inevitably postulate the sacredness of life.

In the same way, the decision to allow an ill patient, suffering from an incurable disease, to expire, given the other demands for the scarce resources of hospital space and equipment and medical skill, postulates the sanctity of life.

Such problems are evidence, not of any denial of the sanctity of life, but rather of its affirmation and its insufficiency.

practice [3]—to impose a given course of action without considering the will and assent of the patient or his legitimate custodian.

Additional considerations arise when we come to artificial insemination (AID), artificial inovulation, and "genetic engineering." "Genetic engineering" and artificial human inovulation are at present only prospects, and the former is not even a near one: they are not yet real issues. It is, however, appropriate to discuss them at this point because they are the center of the apprehensions which are aroused by other forms of contrived intervention. They affect not the vitality of the living human being but rather the process of procreation and the continuity of the lineage.

AID does, and artificial inovulation and genetic engineering would, intrude into and disrupt the lineage; they provide a "descendant" who is not in a direct genetic line with his ancestors. Of course, there have always been variant forms of adoption which introduced a genetically alien element into the lineage, but they have been marginal or superficial in the depth of their entry into the process. The new or prospective forms of intervention penetrate into the center of the process and they therewith affront the primordial sentiment of the sacredness of the stream of life passed down through member-

[3] The development of experimental techniques in medical research raises grave issues. A few medical research workers sometimes proceed in disregard of these issues, but within the medical profession itself, there is also serious scrutiny and criticism of this disregard. Much information and deep reflections on the whole problem are to be found in the writings of Henry K. Beecher of the Massachusetts General Hospital and Harvard University.

ship in a common physiological substance. They create a human being who lacks the genetic continuity with the line of descent of those who take him (or her) as a child.[4]

The genetic manipulator or the artificial inseminator or inovulator is not a member of the lineage; like the organism he helps into existence, he stands outside the stream of primordial continuity. His motives might be sacrilegious; they might with equal likelihood be benevolent; or he might be profoundly neutral, concerned only with the efficient performance of an assigned and accepted task. But unless it becomes possible to produce a fetus and bring it to human life outside a human uterus, the process cannot be carried out without the consent of the woman who is to bear the child. The situation is therefore identical in this respect to the situation which obtains traditionally between patient and physician. The physician does not do what the patient does not agree to allow him to do.[5] It is true that the sanctity of the lineage, which is derivative from the sanctity of life, is infringed by these procedures.

[4] It is impossible for me to say whether this lack of a sense of genetic continuity with "parents" would result in damage to the individuals who would be or are created by this process. The attitudes of adopted children to the discovery of the fact that their "parents" are not really their parents, should be studied. Nonetheless, if it were found that the discovery that foster parents are not real parents has a traumatic effect, that still might not outweigh the advantages of adoption in view of the available alternatives.

[5] The problem is somewhat complicated by whether the husband knows and consents to the artificial insemination or inovulation. But whatever the laws of adultery, they take a stand on problems of identical character.

Yet I do not think that the matter must be taken too tragically. Like religious sensitivity and the powers of reason, the sense of the sacredness of the lineage is unevenly distributed among human beings. Most human beings possess it: some to a very high degree and others only slightly. Some persons even react against it violently. There are certainly many parents who do not care about their children, children who do not care about their parents, and human beings who do not care about their ancestry. For them, what to many of us appears to be an act of impiety, is utterly neutral. There is no reason why they should not be permitted to act on the basis of this "lineage-neutrality." The principle of the sanctity of life is not so univocal and the objects and situations to which it applies are not so unitary that infringements on the integrity of lineage such as we have mentioned call for extreme and unqualified condemnation.

One of the great developments of modern society, and one which many people think—quite rightly—represents a tremendous step forward in human progress, has been the diminution of the weight attributed to lineage as a criterion by which to estimate the value of a human being. The decline in aristocracy, the shrinkage of the realm and power of hereditary monarchy, are expressions of the decline of the importance attributed to lineage. The heightened appreciation of individuality, the enhanced estimation of individual achievement, the growth of civility—the high evaluation of the *individual's* membership in the civil community and of his rights as an individual which come from living under a common

24

authority in a contiguous and bounded territory—the idea of the "career open to talents" and of the corresponding principle of equality of individual opportunity, all attest to the attenuation of "lineage-consciousness" in the advanced societies of modern times. We are living in an epoch in which the center of gravity of the sanctity of life has been displaced from the sanctity of the lineage of genetically linked individual lives to the individuality of discrete human organisms. I do not think that we can have it both ways in every respect, and, of the two, I myself value more highly the emphasis which has become predominant in the modern age.

Furthermore, I doubt whether artificial inovulation will be practiced on a large scale. It seems unlikely that the sense of the sanctity of lineage will die out to such an extent that large numbers of men and women would wish to resort to contrived intervention to provide them with offspring. But there will surely be some who, like those who adopt children, will be willing to have children who are not of their own genetic line. Hence, once it becomes possible, it will occur. If artificial inovulation is to occur, it is most important that it be done under morally legitimate auspices, for good reasons, and with the agreement of the "parents" who agree *irrevocably* to treat the product as their own legitimate offspring with full rights as such and with the fullest protection of the law.

The same may be said of "genetic engineering," if and when that becomes possible. If mature adults, who wish to reduce the probability of the occurrence of clearly hereditary

25

physical and mental defects in their offspring and descendants, seek the aid of a "genetic engineer" to attain this end, I see no more objection to it than to the recourse of afflicted persons to the more conventional types of medical therapy. Their respect for the past of their lineage should be balanced with a concern for its future and for the vital quality of the individual members of its temporal extension.

Once more we see that the sanctity of human life is an equivocal criterion. The value it prizes takes a variety of forms, not all of which are in all ways harmonious with each other. But since it unambiguously entails the vitality and individuality of the living, and the persistence of a lineage into the future, "genetic engineering," if and when it becomes possible, seems to me to be quite acceptable. I assume, of course, that it would be done only on the initiative or with the complete and informed consent of the persons immediately affected and that it would be done by medically qualified persons.

Observance of the sacredness of the lineage is not to be coercively imposed any more than observance of the ritual of any particular religion. If there are persons whose feelings about the sacredness of the lineage are not intense, and if they have good reasons—such as concern for the health of their prospective offspring—there are no grounds for denying them the right to discontinue certain components of their genetic line. "Negative eugenics," which involves forebearance to marry where the union would with high probability bring forth organically defective offspring, is surely compatible with an appreciation of the sanctity of life. It is even required by that appreciation. The same may be said of "genetic engineering." "Genetic engineering" will probably not even involve a complete break with the line. After all, it is not illegal, even if it is not "natural," to remain celibate and to bring one's lineage to extinction. There should correspondingly be no legal or moral grounds for denying these persons the right to disaffiliate their offspring, partially or wholly, from their lineage. As in regular medical and surgical practice, the protection of morally legitimate auspices, good reasons, and a completely voluntary decision on the part of the persons immediately involved, must be observed.

As regards the sanctity of life itself, the biological-technological innovations we have been considering do not diminish life, they improve it. They do not constrict it, rather they enlarge it as far as individual human beings are concerned. It is certainly true that they would intervene, prospectively, at points where it was—and still is—impossible to intervene. But except for the disruption of lineage, they do nothing other than increase and enlarge the vitality of oncoming generations.

Conceivably they could do worse. They might produce a new species of monsters, less intelligent and more destructive than the present species. They might engender a species more sickly, more subject to ailments of every kind, unviable and unworthy. There is fear that they might, but I do not regard this fear as well-founded. Pharmacists could poison the human race; conspiracies of physicians and pharmacists could, even with their present technology, do extraordinary harm to humanity. Surgeons could do the same. At present they do not, and do not intend to do so. Why do they not exploit their present powers? The answer seems almost self-evident: They stand in reverence of life. They are horrified by the possibility of destruction—or they would be horrified if they thought of the possibilities. Of course, there could be the "mad physicians" whom science-fiction brings before us, and there have been the wicked and sadistic physicians who conducted "experiments" in the Nazi concentration camps. There is, however, no reason to expect these cases to become uncontrollably frequent, as long as a civil society endures, the civil authorities are reasonably humane and alert, and the present ethical traditions of the medical and scientific professions continue.

It is possible, of course, that greater potentialities for evil in the future will prove more tempting than the present more limited potentialities. It is also possible that medical education, because of the greatly increased numbers with which it will have to deal in the future, will be less successful than it now is in training into the new members of the profession that ethos which at present sustains the general appreciation of the sanctity of life.

What about the possibility of certain medically unqualified scientists evading the controls which might be quite effective in the medical profession itself? On this point I see no reason why the law should not be able to proceed against these persons as it proceeds at present against those who practice medicine without the necessary qualifications, or who, having the qualifications, behave in a clearly unethical and professionally pernicious manner.

Thus far we have discussed the prolongation or "creation" of life. But what about its annihilation through abortion and euthanasia? Are such actions morally permissible from a standpoint which regards life as sacred? In principle, I have little doubt about abortion, considerable doubt about euthanasia.

My reasons are as follows. The postulate of the sanctity of life refers to three forms of life: (1) the life of the lineage; (2) the life of the human organism; and (3) the life of the individual human being, as an individuality located in a discrete organism, possessing consciousness of itself as an agent and patient both in the past and present, having the capacity for psychic "self-locomotion" (i.e., capacities for perception, the amalgamation and ordering of perceptions, the storage and recall of cognitive, moral, and appreciative patterns, and the ability to choose and intend).

A fetus, for much of the period of gestation, does not qualify for the sanctity which is attributed to life. It is still organically part of the mother; it has not begun to learn from its own experience and the symbolic communication of others, and it has therefore not started on the path to individuality. It is not yet an individual life—it is part of the life of the mother. It is not, it is true, a part in the same way as a limb

29

or an internal organ are parts of a living human organism, but it also is not yet a separate human organism beginning to remember, to discriminate, to intend. What it "knows," it "knows" by an inherited genetic "code." An infant is on the path to the development of individuality, which is more than biological uniqueness. A fetus is at a much earlier stage on the path, on which actual birth is the decisive turning.

There are many good reasons to regret abortion or the necessity for it—effective contraception would be much more satisfactory—but I think that for our purposes it should be said that the principle of the sanctity of life of the individual as an individual, or the life of the lineage as the lineage of separate organisms, is not infringed or affronted by abortion in the earlier stages of pregnancy. The point in the period of gestation where the permissible becomes problematic is not easily determinable, but this does not weaken the principle which asserts that abortion within certain limits is compatible with the sanctity of life.

When we come to euthanasia of monsters or extreme idiots, the matter seems to me to be much more difficult. In the first place we are dealing with discrete human organisms which have by their separateness and by their human generation a close resemblance to other members of the species; by virtue of their membership in that species and the mode of their generation, they have a putative capacity for individuality. If we affirm the principle of the sanctity of life, euthanasia in marginal cases of idiocy or monstrosity is reprehensible, and in extreme cases too it is repugnant. I

30

am unwilling to see euthanasia embodied in laws which authorize it, but I would have much sympathy for a flexible attitude in the courts toward those unfortunates whose solicitous and unhappy love drives them to commit "mercy killings."

At the other end of the life span, where there is a certainly dying person in great pain, with not even the slightest probability of recovery, and where individuality has ceased totally to exist, euthanasia is even more repugnant to our sense of the sanctity of life. Nonetheless, it must be admitted that certain current practices are almost tantamount to euthanasia. In some respects the fact of scarcity of medical resources permits a solution which approximates, but is not identical with, euthanasia—namely, suspension of effort to keep the organism alive. The argument against authorizing euthanasia seems to me to rest less in the nature of the action itself and more in the deficiencies of our knowledge in assessing the absence or cessation of individuality—itself so ambiguous as to defy clear definitions—and in our distrust of the wisdom and generosity of men. The situation is bound to become more trying in the quite near future as the power to prolong a minimum of life while not restoring a large measure of vitality increases. The enhancement of the capacity to keep the organism alive where that capacity did not exist before, will raise the issue far more challengingly than it was ever raised when medical capacities were slighter. I do not think that an affirmation of the sanctity of life requires that a badly functioning human organism, which is certainly incurable and doomed never to recover consciousness or to escape extreme pain, be kept alive—in the sense of breathing and pulsating—when nothing more than that can be accomplished. The real question here seems less one of principle than of finding the consensus of responsible medical opinion which can attest without qualification that individuality has ceased to exist and cannot be restored.

The sanctity of individuality is a variant form of the sanctity of life. The ambiguities of the ideas of individuality and "normality" or "naturalness" hamper our judgment when we consider another form of "contrived intervention" and when we attempt to do justice to the abhorrence which many persons experience when confronted with certain developments in psychiatric, neurosurgical, and psychological technology. At the same time, the aversion against the taking of narcotics, the administration of hallucinogenic drugs, the use of devices for stimulating subliminal perception and for secretly observing and recording occurrences in the private sphere, seems to be an aversion against the infringement on individuality. It arises from an anxiety lest the individual be made into something other than he "is." It is a fear that the particularly individuated and differentiated current of life which exists in the individual human organism will be tampered with, damaged, or extinguished. It is not that the individuality of particular human beings is always taken as given and final; the individuality of particular human beings and classes of human beings certainly is and has been regarded as subject to certain legitimate modes of influence. The guidance and formation of character through education and domestic discipline, the depressive and stunting effects of poverty and maltreatment, and the transformation of sensibility and mental powers through alcohol and sedative drugs are all widely, although unequally, accepted. The stimulation of the imagination through literature and drama is accepted, but not the pharmacological stimulation of the imagination. The deadening of impulse through poverty and loneliness is also accepted—although decreasingly so—but not the deadening of sensibility through narcotics. The heightening of the power of the senses of vision, touch, taste through training is accepted, but not their heightening through drugs.

Some of this acceptance of deformations of individuality is a function of the compellingness of the inevitable, or at least of the apparently unchangeable; some is also a function of insensitivity, of an insufficient sympathy with the state of mind of others. But this acceptance is also—and this is the most relevant point for our discussion—a function of a conception of "normality." It is the product of a metaphysical belief in a pre-established and inviolable pattern of individuality which may coexist with certain externally imposed influences but not with others. Those with which coexistence is not possible are the deliberate ones, those which are contrived and do not arise from the course of "normal" interaction and the inevitabilities of existence. It is the element of deliberate deformation of "normal" consciousness which renders abhorrent the administration of drugs to the self; it is the deliberate and deceptive manipulation of conduct by experimental means not understood by the participant-subject of an experiment which renders such practices abhorrent. The concept of "normality" presupposes an "essential form" in which individuality exists. Slow and imperceptible processes of change or influence are not regarded as repugnant to this conception of normality because they are not seen as "abnormal" or "unnatural" and because they do not obviously impinge on individuality. Changing oneself deliberately by the exertion of internal moral resources, or by the adduction of certain external, allegedly "sacred," influences of moral and religious guidance, by placing one's self in a flow of symbolic communication, e.g., literary works, is all right. The anonymous influence of social class on moral and cultural attitudes is also all right; religious conversion is all right. They are regarded as all right because they take place in a medium of an "essential form" of human interaction, in friendship, in work, in worship, and so forth, which is assumed to be given. Much of the content of this "essential form" may be accounted for by the statistical frequency and consequently conventional normativeness of the practices in question. But the frequency and conventionality might themselves be functions of their possession of the property of "essential form." They occur frequently because they are thought to be "normal." This "essential form" or "normality" is vaguely conceived, and it permits a wide range of acceptable variation.

But one of the things it excludes is the complete dominion of one human being over another, or the complete renunciation of control over one's self, whether it be renunciation to another person or to some chemical agent. The loss or renunciation of all individual autonomy by the dominated or abdicating person is the decisive element here. Autonomy, thus understood, is what the individual would be if left alone to the extent that he is by his kinship group, his working colleagues, his neighbors, and his rulers. There is often not much of him left over after this, but what remains is his temperament and his memory of his own individual past. When these are taken away from him by "contrived intervention," or by his cooperation, or even by his own deliberate choice, other persons who do not participate in the complete dominion or abdication experience a sense of abhorrence.

Under what conditions is the modification of temperament and individuality by "contrived intervention" permissible? It is certainly not permissible as a satisfaction of the curiosity of psychologists who wish to see how far the personality can be modified by pharmaceutical or neurosurgical means. It is obviously not permissible for political purposes, such as the maintenance of public order, or for the protection of the unchallenged dominion of the rulers of society or any particular organization within society. Is it permissible for therapeutic ends? I see no argument against this, as long as the usual safeguards practiced by the medical profession are observed, i.e., as long as the informed consent of the patient, or of his kinsmen who are morally responsible for him, is given. Where an individual has already lost such individuality as he once possessed, and where the therapeutic technique offers a reasonable probability of the restoration to him of some part of his previous individuality, it seems to me to be morally unexceptionable.

The protection necessary for the sanctity of individuality depends in part on the strength of the ethical consensus of the medical and life-science professions and on the formation of a comparable ethical outlook among psychologists, social workers, and related professions. It thus depends on the moral vigilance and responsibility of the universities and particularly of those who are in charge of training in biology, medicine, psychology, sociology, and social work. It depends also on the vigilance of legislators and the courts in specifying and clarifying the range of permissible interventions and implementing strict prohibition on attempts to modify individuality by persons without adequate professional qualifications. The sanctity of individuality depends, therefore, on public opinion: this means that it depends on the initiative of philosophers, theologians, lawyers, legislators, sociologists, physicians, molecular biologists *et al.*, in bringing the issues into clearer focus and in stimulating serious public discussion.

This brief examination of the range and limits of what is permissible in "contrived intervention" brings us back to where we began. Without a widespread affirmation of the sanctity of life—and of the variant forms of the sanctity of life such as the sanctity of individuality—as a basic and guiding principle of social life, we will be hopelessly adrift. The crisis is not fully upon us, because the techniques of "contrived intervention" are not yet as elaborate or as secure as they are likely to be in the future. When they do develop more fully and effectively, they will undoubtedly offer stronger temptations for exploitation to those in whom the sense of the sanctity of human life and of human individuality is weak or perverted.

The situation will surely not be made easier by the ambiguity and the inherent tensions and contradictions of the idea of the sanctity of life. By its very structure, this fundamental moral principle cannot provide an absolutely unambiguous guide which will indicate infallibly what is permissible and what is not permissible in any particular case. Nonetheless, it provides the only ultimate foundation for the protection by public and professional opinion and by legislatures and courts against sadism in its more crude and brutal forms, or in the more refined form of allegedly "scientific" curiosity.

Those who accept the traditional Christian view of man and its theological postulates encounter no difficulty in the way of affirming the sanctity of life, although its application will often present dilemmas which are inherent in the idea itself. For those who no longer accept the traditional Christian view, the acceptance of the idea of the sanctity of life

37

might well present intellectual obstacles. I myself find no such obstacles, and I do not think that there are any in the conception of sanctity which I have put forward here.

From my point of view, the task of our generation and those immediately following is not so much the re-establishment of a Christianity which is shorn of its historical and mythological accretions, but rather the rediscovery of what it was that for so long gave such persuasive power to Christianity. In our culture this powerful impulse became so intimately fused with Christian doctrine and belief that now, when Christianity has become in varying degrees unacceptable to many educated persons, the prior and impelling belief in the sanctity of man's life and personality has also seemed to lose its acceptability. But the powerful impulses will remain, and that is why the protoreligion, the "natural metaphysic" of the sanctity of life, must be intellectually rehabilitated and rendered acceptable.

Law and the Moral Consensus

THE IDEA of law in the common-law tradition is inseparably connected with morals. In the past, religion played the role fulfilled by morality today. In origin, the common law was a specifically English creation shaped by the old religion and the national character. The new religion drove out the old and in its turn was superseded by secularism. As a result, theological questions have been pushed from the legal center to the margins. They may still, of course, be raised, but they can only contribute to the argument, not determine it. Theology in our pluralist society is no longer a queen but a subject. She has the right to raise her voice but sovereignty has passed elsewhere.

Thus, in a community made up of men who hold different religious beliefs, or none at all, religion can make no claims

NORMAN ST.JOHN-STEVAS

to be society's common bond. But bond there must be, for without it society would be merely an agglomeration of warring individuals. Western society in general, and Anglo-American society in particular, is held together today by a common morality. Of course, there are wide differences of view on individual moral issues, and tolerance of these is in itself a moral value and a distinguishing feature of our society; but agreement over a range of moral attitudes there is and must be. J. H. Newman called this agreement society's *common possession*. For Newman, society was "a collection of many individuals made one by their participation in some common possession, and to the extent of that common possession, the presence of that possession held in common constitutes the life, and the loss of it constitutes the dissolution, of a state." [1] Walter Lippmann uses the term "public philosophy" to express the same idea.

Law both reflects and preserves the moral consensus of society. The very notion of law, that disputes should be settled by order and rule, is itself a civilized value. Force is the ultimate sanction even of law, but law is obeyed by the majority as much because it is felt to be morally binding as because of the knowledge that breach will lead to punishment. This is demonstrated by the fact that positive law in a free society ultimately loses its efficacy if it ceases to correspond with what Ehrlich has called "the living law" of society, the underlying beliefs and habits of a people. Law rests on the sentiment and the will of the governed, and if correspondence ceases, the law can no longer be enforced. A good illustration of this relationship is provided by the English law governing dissemination of contraceptive information. Books imparting such information were considered obscene in the nineteenth century, but legal sanctions are no longer used against them. No formal change was made in the law, which was quietly allowed to lapse as far as these books were concerned, the reason being that contraception had obtained general moral acceptance in the community. Again, in countries which have formally abolished capital punishment, the death penalty has generally been abandoned in practice for some time before actual legislative abolition.

The *common good* or *moral consensus* of a society will be

[1] J. H. Newman, *Historical Sketches* (London, 1872–73), I, 161.

reflected in legislation or constitutional documents, but much of it, being "the wisdom of a great society" transmitted over the generations, will not be reduced to written form. It is, writes John Courtney Murray, "the intuitional *a priori* of all the rationalities and technicalities of constitutional and statutory law. It furnishes the premises of the people's action in history and defines the larger aims which that action seeks in internal affairs and public relations." Three points should be made here. First, not all of the moral consensus will be enforced by law, although the law will always take account of it.² It may, for example, be agreed that homosexuality is immoral, in which case the law will give no countenance to homosexual relationships; but at the same time it may well be agreed that because a prohibitory law may not be enforceable, or not enforceable equitably, or may give rise to greater evils than those it is intended to eradicate, homosexual acts should not be criminal offenses. Second, the moral consensus is not given for all time. It will change as society changes, but the likelihood is that the law in moral matters will be a conservative rather than a revolutionary influence, eventually reflecting changed moral views rather than promoting them. Third, the law cannot guarantee ultimate rightness. It sys-

² Hence, St. Thomas Aquinas pointed out that it was not the function of the law to promote every virtue or to forbid every vice, but to forbid only the more grievous vices from which it was possible for the majority of imperfect human beings to abstain, "and chiefly those that are to the hurt of others, without the prohibition of which society could not be maintained: thus human law prohibits murder, theft, and suchlike" (*Summa Theologica*, I–II, Q. 16, arts. 2 and 3).

tematizes consciences and to that extent has moral authority, but consciences can err. The law is nothing less nor more than the collective conscience of the community on those issues which it is felt cannot be left to individual choice. It cannot provide infallible rules of moral guidance.

What is the content of our present moral consensus, especially in relation to law? This is not the place for an exhaustive catalogue, but one can point to some concepts and propositions. Concepts which direct the dynamism of the common law include those of fairness, reasonableness, and observance of the rules of natural justice. Propositions deducible from the law and to which society gives wide assent are, for example, that every man should be free to practice his own religion, that private property should be respected, that marriage, subject to exceptions, should be a permanent union. One concept which is presumed by every branch of the law but which is reflected most clearly and directly in the criminal law is that of the sanctity of life. It is implicit in the common-law idea of man as *liber et legalis homo:* it becomes explicit in the great series of declarations of the rights of man from the American revolution to our own day. "We hold these truths to be self-evident," proclaims the Declaration of Independence, "that all men are created equal, that they are endowed by their Creator with certain unalienable Rights, that among these are Life, Liberty and the pursuit of Happiness."

The concept of a right to life requires more precise formulation. Clearly, it refers only to human life: the law has imposed duties on man in his dealings with animals, but it has never endowed animals with rights. Medieval law was dominated by the idea of natural law, our own by the assumption of the existence of human rights. This is reinforced by modern man's psychological awareness of his own uniqueness. The law assumes the value of human life as a fact: it does not seek to explain it. The law's acceptance of the fact is deeply rooted in experience and history. It is rooted especially in religion and the Christian doctrine of man as a person, a union of body and soul destined for eternal life. The fact that the concept of the sanctity of human life has a theological foundation is not invalidated by the rejection of that foundation by many in the West today. "It has got there," as Sir Patrick Devlin says of the permanent marriage contract, "because it is Christian, but it remains there because it is built into the house in which we live and could not be removed without bringing it down." [3]

The acceptance of this concept by the law has made a profound difference to our society. It is the premise not only of liberty but of equality and fraternity. Other legal systems have confined the principle of the sanctity of life to a class or classes of people within society. Whole sections can be excluded, as in the great slave empires of the pre-Christian era or Hitler's "new order" of our own time. The uniqueness of our legal concept lies in its universality.

This is not to say that Western society has maintained that

[3] Patrick Devlin, *The Enforcement of Morals* (London and New York: Oxford University Press, 1965), p. 9.

under no circumstances may human life be taken. There have been widely accepted exceptions: under certain circumstances the state has the right to take life, and the taking of life in war can under certain conditions also be justified. The principle which the Western world has accepted in theory and embodied in its law, although it has certainly not always lived up to it in practice, is that—self-defense against aggressors apart—human life may not be taken. The principle is that innocent human life is sacred.

When does the right to life begin? At one time the law attempted to protect even potential human life by penalizing and prohibiting contraception. In England the position was abandoned after the Bradlaugh-Besant trial of 1877, and in the United States after the First World War. Isolated pockets of resistance in states such as Connecticut and Massachusetts have not been of great legal or social significance. Condemnation of contraception is no longer part of the public moral consensus, and the issue has therefore been rightly relegated to the private sphere, to be resolved by individuals according to their consciences.

Anglo-American law has traditionally protected the life of the unborn child: it does not wait until birth to extend recognition of a right to life. At the same time, killing a fetus has not been regarded as murder: for that, the victim must be "in being," that is, born. Abortion or the expulsion of a living fetus from the uterus before the twenty-eighth week of pregnancy, that is, before the fetus becomes viable, is a crime. According to Coke in his Institutes, abortion was considered by the common law to be "a great misprision" or misdemeanor. Today it is a statutory offense in England and in all American legal jurisdictions. There is, however, in England and in many American states an important limitation to the law, declared in Bourne's case in 1939. The position appears to be that if an abortion is considered necessary to preserve the life of the mother or to protect her from a serious threat to health, then it is not a crime. Anglo-American law, therefore, extends its protection to human life from the moment of conception and will only withdraw it when that life threatens another, which is considered more valuable because of the higher stage of development it has reached.

This attitude of the law toward the fetus reflects the general moral consensus in the community which, while it stops short of equating the fetus with a human person, agrees that as a living human organism—a potential life—the fetus has rights which should be respected. These rights should only be taken away when they cause a conflict with the rights of the mother and there is no other way of protecting her. This is an application of the legal doctrine of necessity. As conditions of *necessity*, it is required that the evil averted by the operation must be greater than the evil performed; and that no more evil may be done than is reasonably necessary to avert the greater evil.[4]

The present law is now under attack from two standpoints.

[4] See *Decisions about Life and Death* (London: C.I.O., 1965), Appendix 2: "The Common Law Doctrine of Necessity," by E. Garth Moore.

First, Roman Catholics and others maintain that the fetus should in virtually all respects be treated as possessing the rights of a human person. Basing their view on contemporary biology, which accepts that there is no qualitative difference between the embryo at the moment of conception and at the moment of quickening, they hold that life is fully present from the moment of conception. It follows that, if there be a soul, it too is probably present from the time of conception. Killing a fetus is therefore theologically murder, whatever the law may say.[5] Others assail the law from a completely different point of view. Some go so far as to maintain that a woman has an unfettered right to an abortion, although no legal system has recognized it. Others campaign for abortion to be allowed not only on health grounds, but for social and eugenic reasons. These views have made some headway recently in England. In 1967 the British Parliament passed an abortion bill which would not only allow abortion on health grounds, but also if there is a "substantial risk" that if the child were born "it would suffer from such physical or mental abnormalities as to be seriously handicapped" or if there is a risk that the health of "any existing children of [the mother's] family" might be adversely affected by the birth of another child.

[5] Some Roman Catholics, however, hold the theory of "mediate animation," which maintains that the first life present is vegetative not human, and that the soul is not infused until the body is sufficiently developed to receive it. Even if this view is held, the "vegetative" life is worthy of protection as potential human life which will eventually be transformed into a human being.

The Act makes radical departures from what has hitherto been considered the moral consensus on the matter. Sacrificing the life of the fetus to protect the mother is one thing; depriving it of life because of prognostication of abnormality is quite different. In the first place, how can "likely" be established with sufficient certainty in the present state of medical knowledge? [6] More important, the Act presumes a right to take innocent human life where no argument from "necessity" can apply. It presupposes that one human being can judge whether another potential life is worth living and enforce that judgment, a power that has never been conferred by our law On medical and moral grounds, then, such a change in the law seems unacceptable. It would indeed be more logical to wait until the child was born and see whether it was deformed before disposing of it.

This was the exact situation in the now famous Liège case of 1962. In that case Madame Suzanne Vandeput was tried for the murder of her eight-day-old daughter, born deformed as a result of her mother's taking the drug thalidomide during pregnancy. She was acquitted. Whatever the merits of this acquittal on the grounds of sentiment, it struck an unintended blow at the principle of the sanctity of life. Every child, how-

[6] The following story, which was told by Maurice Baring, is of some relevance. One doctor to another: "About the terminating of pregnancy, I want your opinion. The father was syphilitic. The mother tuberculous. Of the four children born, the first was blind, the second died, the third was deaf and dumb, the fourth was also tuberculous. What would you have done?" "I would have ended the pregnancy." "Then you would have murdered Beethoven."

ever deformed or handicapped, has a fundamental right to life, which neither the individual nor the state has any moral claim to take away. Whether the child will be useful to society is, strictly speaking, irrelevant, although there is strong evidence to suggest that what at first sight look like insuperable handicaps can in fact be overcome. The second principle breached by the Vandeput case is that, immediate self-defense apart, the taking of life should be confined to the state. The case in effect confers a license to kill on the individual citizen, a license furthermore with no clear limiting terms. To one person, life without sight will appear unbearable; to another, the absence of arms; to another, the lack of legs. The law has held fast to the principle that only in the most closely defined circumstances may life be taken, and then only by the state. For this rigorous criterion the Vandeput case substitutes the standard of personal taste. One final point may be made here. The protestations that the motives of those who kill deformed children are unselfish and benevolent, are in themselves open to question. Whose sufferings are being spared, those of the child or those of its relatives who would have to look after it and care for it? What kind of society is it that prefers to obliterate suffering rather than relieve it? [7]

One argument that is often advanced for extending legalized abortion is that it would reduce the number of illegal

[7] For an account of the trial and the correspondence it evoked in *The Times*, see *The Acquittals at Liège*, a pamphlet published by *The Times* in 1963.

abortions and get rid of the back-street abortionist. Women will have abortions anyhow, runs the argument, and they might as well have them under hygienic conditions instead of using knitting needles in a back parlor. Before this argument can be evaluated, it is necessary to know the number of illegal abortions; but there are no reliable statistics for these, only guesses. The estimates for the English rate range from ten thousand to one hundred thousand per year. In any case, such evidence as there is shows that widening the legal grounds for abortion does not reduce the illegal rate. In Sweden, where abortion is allowed for a wide range of medico-social and eugenic reasons, this does not appear to have had the effect of reducing the illegal rate, as had been hoped. The only way of getting rid of the back-street abortionist is to remove restrictions on abortion altogether. No country has done this, but Japan, which has moved nearest to it, found that the abortion rate increased so rapidly as to threaten the whole future of the nation. Abortions after 1948 averaged a million a year, the age structure of the population became seriously distorted, health risks to mothers were increased, and in 1952 the government sponsored a campaign to replace abortion by contraception. There is now a parliamentary movement in Japan to restrict abortion once again and to punish mothers and physicians in cases where abortion is induced without medical reasons.

The restriction of abortion and the condemnation of compulsory euthanasia by the law both derive support from their involving a violation of the rights of others. But what of suicide or *voluntary* euthanasia? These are in a different category, since they involve no violation of another's rights but only the voluntary surrender of an individual's own rights. The law has traditionally forbidden both. Is this justified?

Some maintain that it is not: that the state has no right to enforce morality or penalize immorality unless this in some way interferes with the rights of others. This view received its classic formulation in John Stuart Mill's treatise on liberty. Mill laid down his principle in these words:

> . . . the sole end for which mankind are warranted, individually or collectively, in interfering with the liberty of their number, is self-protection. That the only purpose for which power can be rightfully exercised over any member of a civilized community, against his will, is to prevent harm to others. His own good, either physical or moral, is not a sufficient warrant. He cannot be compelled to do or forbear because it will be better for him to do so, because it will make him happier, because in the opinion of others, to do so would be wise, or even right.[8]

What Mill appears to have meant by "harm to others" was principally physical harm to other individuals.

Against Mill's thesis can be advanced the view, elaborated most comprehensively by Sir Patrick Devlin, that the moral ideas held by the community are a legitimate object of legal protection and enforcement.[9] Principles such as the respect for the sanctity of life are part of the common good. If they are

---

[8] John Stuart Mill, *On Liberty* (1859). Reprinted in *Utilitarianism, Liberty and Representative Government* (Everyman's Library, No. 482; London, 1910), p. 72.

[9] Devlin, *The Enforcement of Morals*, especially chaps. i, v, vi, and vii.

undermined by behavior, whether private or public, society— and eventually the individuals who compose it—is harmed. This is to postulate a right to enforce morality by law, but not to say that it should be exercised in every instance. It becomes a question of balance. To legalize suicide and euthanasia, for example, might well have the effect of weakening respect for the sanctity of human life, which is part of our moral consensus. On the other hand, to impose criminal sanctions is useless, causes unnecessary suffering, and has harmful social effects. The arguments have to be weighed and a decision taken as to where the balance of advantage or disadvantage lies.

Recently the English law on suicide has been changed. In 1961 a statute was passed under which suicide ceased to be a criminal offense, as did attempts at the act. This brought English law into line with that in most American states. The common law had penalized suicide because it was regarded as a deliberate and wicked flouting of God's will. In 1563 in Hales's case, the judge declared that suicide is against nature, "because it is contrary to the rules of self-preservation, which is the principle of nature, for everything living does by instinct of nature defend itself from destruction, and then to destroy one's self is contrary to nature and a thing most horrible." He went on to state that it was an offense against God, "in that it is a breach of His commandment *Thou shalt not kill;* and to kill himself, by which act he kills in presumption his own soul, is a greater offence than to kill another." The judge's third reason for condemning suicide was that the king lost a subject, "he being the head has lost one of his mystical members." Another judge in the case added that suicide should be punished because it set an evil example which might be followed by others.[10]

English law has changed because medical and sociological research has established that suicide is a much more complicated act than the simple analysis in Hales's case allowed. Émile Durkheim has shown that suicide is a phenomenon caused at least in part by social conditions.[11] Egotistic suicide, for example, results from the lack of integration of the individual into society, the suicide rate increasing with the degree that the individual is thrown onto his own resources. Thus, at a period of national crisis such as war, suicide rates fall, since the emergency provides greater opportunity for participation in the life of the community. Freud, on the other hand, explained suicide not as the outcome of immediate social conditions, but of long pent-up aggressive and guilt feelings in an emotionally immature person.[12] On either view the freedom of the suicidal act is much diminished. Attempted suicide has also been the subject of research, and it is now reasonably established that many so-called attempts are not so much genuine efforts to end life as appeals for help.[13] In suicide the penal

[10] *Hales v. Petit*, 1 Plow. 253, 75 E.R. 387 (C.B. 1563).

[11] Émile Durkheim, *Suicide: A Study in Sociology* (London, 1952).

[12] See Sigmund Freud "Mourning and Melancholia," *Collected Papers* (London, 1925), Vol. IV.

[13] E. Stengel and Nancy Cook, *Attempted Suicide: Social Significance and Effects* (London, 1958). See also "Recent Research into Suicide and Attempted Suicide," *Journal of Forensic Medicine*, I (1953–54), 252.

sanction is virtually useless: in attempted suicide it is positively harmful, since it may well deter attempters and their relatives from seeking skilled help. These considerations have proved decisive. The threat to the principle of the sanctity of life by legalizing suicide has been adjudged too remote and insubstantial to justify retaining irrelevant and harmful criminal sanctions.

On voluntary euthanasia the balance has tilted the other way. The complicating social and psychological factors which have to be taken into account when considering suicide are not present in euthanasia. The spectacle of the law lending active assistance in voluntary extinction of life might well undermine respect for human life in general. No one has found a satisfactory means of invoking the law's aid. Schemes which involve appeal to a "Euthanasia Referee" and deathbed witnesses to the dispatch of the applicant strike most people as cumbrous and cold-blooded, if not bloodcurdling. The scope for abuse by interested parties need not be stressed. Against these arguments may be ranged the relief from pain and suffering that would be brought about. Fortunately, modern medicine has already revolutionized this aspect of dying, and further progress is constantly being made. Doctors do not uselessly prolong the life of those who are dying: pain-killing drugs which may have the unintended side effect of shortening life are used widely and quite ethically. The problem is best regulated not by the clumsy instrument of the law but by the medical profession itself. The good doctor, as Lord Horder

55

has stated, is aware of the distinction between prolonging life and prolonging the act of dying.[14]

A final issue which involves the principle of the sanctity of life is that of capital punishment. It strikes the modern man as strange that a system of law built around respect for human life should have countenanced capital punishment for so long. Such a view is unhistorical. Murder was visited with the capital penalty precisely because it was felt to be so heinous a crime that no lesser punishment was appropriate. In societies where life was constantly threatened and police forces rudimentary, the death penalty was thought of as a necessary deterrent. The moral consensus has always been that the state has the right to take the life of an unjust aggressor if this is a necessary means of the state's maintaining itself and order. The relevant principle has been that of self-defense. Just as the law has allowed an individual to take another's life if he is unjustly attacked, so that right has been conceded to the state. In the case of individuals, however, the common law has always insisted that taking the life of another person should be the only means of self-defense open to the person attacked. If a lesser degree of force suffices, it should be employed. This limitation applies also to the state. The question then becomes not whether there is a right in the state to take life, but whether the right should be exercised. This is a question that can only be answered after an exhaustive consideration of the facts and social conditions involved, but it may be said

[14] House of Lords Debates (5th series), 103: 490 (1936).

that today a heavy burden of proof rests upon the state to justify a policy of capital punishment.

A wide range of arguments can be marshaled against the use of the death penalty—the effect on those who have to carry it out, the danger of a mistake being made which cannot be rectified, the inflexibility of the penalty, and the exclusion of any possibility of reform. Above all, there is the danger that, whatever may have been the case in times past, use of the death penalty today—far from promoting respect for the principle of the sanctity of life—in fact undermines it. "I believe," said Archbishop Temple, "that the example of the state taking life, even when it only does so in return for a life already taken, does more to lower the value of human life in the minds of its citizens than the deterrent influence of this penalty can do to protect the lives of the citizens." In Britain in 1965 Parliament abolished the death penalty. I am happy that I was a member of that Parliament and was able to vote for its ending.

In an age which has placed, through technology, unprecedented power in the hands of man, a view of man's nature is not less necessary and relevant, but more so. Man may know more, but he has never been in greater danger of being dehumanized. To describe these new scientific processes is not my task. I am a lawyer, not a scientist or a geneticist. That duty will be discharged by other expert contributors to this symposium. Yet every layman knows that today drugs can control or alter human personality, that life or reproductive functions can be easily destroyed, that radiation and fallout threaten the future of the human race. If power is there, why should it not be used? My personal belief is that only the Christian doctrine of man can effectively moderate the tyranny of scientific techniques. The Christian view is that man is not absolute master of his own fate, but holds his life and body in trust for other purposes. If this concept places limits on man's independence by stressing that he is the user not the proprietor of life, it also preserves his humanity by erecting barriers beyond which technology cannot pass. Yet faith is given to few, and modern secular man must, it seems, do without it. In this predicament he could do worse than be guided by the wisdom of the common law, with its centuries-old recognition of man's dignity and freedom. An intrinsic constituent of that recognition is respect for the sanctity of human life.

The Morality of Abortion

ALMOST everyone has a proposal to make concerning when in the course of its prenatal or postnatal development embryonic life becomes "human." At one extreme are the views of those who hold that life is not human until the individual is a personal subject or has reason in exercise. If to be human *means* to be a person, to be a self-conscious subject of experience, or if it means to be rational, this state of affairs does not come to pass until a long while after the birth of a baby. A human infant acquires its personhood and self-conscious subjective identity through "Thou–I" encounters with other selves; and a child acquires essential rationality even more laboriously. If life must be human in these senses before it has any sanctity and respect or rights due it, infanticide would seem to be justified under any number of conditions believed to warrant it as permissible behavior or as a social policy. In

60

PAUL RAMSEY

any case, those who identify being human with personhood or rationality adopt a modern form of an ancient theological position called "creationism." According to this view, the unique, never-to-be-repeated individual human being (the "soul" is the religious word for him) comes into existence by a process of humanization or socialization in interaction with the persons around him. In the traditional religious language, he is "created" and "infused" into the already existing organism—sometime, gradually, after physical birth.

At the other extreme is the latest scientific view, that of modern genetics. Indeed, microgenetics seems to have demonstrated what religion never could; and biological science, to have resolved an ancient theological dispute. The human individual comes into existence first as a minute informational speck, drawn at random from many other minute informa-

61

tional specks his parents possessed out of the common human gene pool. This took place at the moment of impregnation. There were, of course, an unimaginable number of combinations of specks on his paternal and maternal chromasomes that did not come to be when they were refused and he began to be. Still (with the single exception of identical twins), no one else in the entire history of the human race has ever had or will ever have exactly the same genotype. Thus, it can be said that the individual is whoever he is going to become from the moment of impregnation. Thereafter, his subsequent development may be described as a process of becoming the one he already is. Genetics teaches that we were from the beginning what we essentially still are in every cell and in every human and individual attribute. This scientific account is a modern form of the ancient theological viewpoint called "traducianism." According to this view, the unique, never-to-be-repeated individual human being (the "soul") was drawn forth from his parents at the time of conception.[1]

---

[1] In order to take care of the case of identical twins (and also to account for the special ways in which our already unique combination of genetic determiners develops over a lifetime), it is necessary, of course, to bring in the modern version of "creationism" to which I have referred. Identical twins have the same genotype. They arise from the same informational speck. Yet each is and knows he is a unique, unrepeatable human person. He is something that he never was by virtue of his genes. He became something, at some time and in some manner, that he was not already, from the fission following that original conception. It is the environment who is the maker of all twin differences and the creator of a twin person's unsharable individual being; after they were born the environment "infused" this into those two blobs of identical hereditary material, which contained not only an incalculable number of powers distinguishing them as human blobs

What is this but to say that we are all fellow fetuses? That from womb to tomb ours is a nascent life? That we are in essence congeners from the beginning? What is this but a rather antiseptic way of saying that the Creator has beset us behind and before? While we know only the light of our particular span of conscious existence, this light and that darkness whence we came and toward which we go are both alike to the One who laid his hands upon us, covered us in the womb, and by whom we were fearfully and wonderfully made.

---

but also an incalculable number of the features of the individual beings each is to spend a whole lifetime becoming and exhibiting.

The case of identical twins does, however, suggest a significant modification of any "proof" from genotype. If there is a moment in the development of nascent life subsequent to impregnation and prior to birth (or graduation from Princeton) at which it would be reasonable to believe that an individual human life *begins* to be inviolate, that moment is arguably at the stage of *blastocyst*. Blastocyst is the appearance of a "primitive streak" across the hollow cluster of developing cells that signals the separation of the same genotype into identical twins. This occurs at about the time of implantation, i.e. on the seventh or eighth day after ovulation. It might be asserted that it is at blastocyst, not earlier, that these two products of human generation become "animate," each a unique individual "soul." This is *not* to say that any credit is to be given to those self-serving arguments that "implantation" is the first moment of "life" having claims upon our respect. These are, in the worst sense of the word, mere rationalizations currently offered for the purpose of rejecting out of hand the proofs that interuterine devices (the "loop") are abortifacient, and that the "morning after" or retroactive pill (which will be available in a year or so) will directly abort a human life. Still, blastocyst (which, as it happens, is roughly coincident with implantation) affords serious moralists a fact concerning nascent life that may and must be taken into account when dealing with the morality of using interuterine devices or a retroactive "contraceptive" pill. This may have bearing on whether the question raised by these scientific applications is one of abortion or of contraception only, or of an attack upon prehuman organic matter.

Between the extremes of "traducianism" at conception and "creationism" gradually after birth, there are other accounts of when the human being originates and thus becomes a subject worthy of respect, rights, sanctity. No one of the positions yet to be mentioned is quite as up-to-date and scientific as the genetic account of the origin of human individuality. Among these are religious and legal viewpoints that seem always to be based on prescientific notions and "superstitions." Anglo-American law, for example, takes the moment of birth to be the moment after which there is a "man alive" (for which the evidence is air in the lungs) and before which there was no human life, separable from the mother's, that could be murdered. When it is born a "man alive," the child is from that moment already the one it ever thereafter becomes; not before, as genetics teaches. After it is born a "man alive," a child is then and then only a possible victim of the crime of "murder."

Where "abortion" is defined as a criminal offense in our legal systems, this creates another category of proscribed actions. It is not because the fetus is regarded as having sanctity or integrity or an independent right to life such as the law presupposes in the case of a "man alive." The legal reason for prohibiting abortion is not because it is believed to be a species of murder; it is the religious tradition, we shall see, and not the law which inculcates the latter view. The law's presumption is only that society has a stake in the prehuman material out of which the unique individual is to be born. Or it may be that the law exhibits a belief that as a matter of public policy society has an interest in *men* and *women*, who have an interest in and by their actions take responsibility for the prehuman material out of which an individual human being is to be brought forth a man alive.

This brings us to the theories advanced by theologians and by church-law—all doubtless to be classed, along with the law, as "superstitious" and prescientific in comparison with the genetic account of the arrival of the essential constitutive features of a human individual. The theologians propose an analysis of the prenatal development of the fetus. This means that they assert that the fetus *before* birth may be the victim of the sin of "murder." But this does not immediately entail that *any* destruction of fetal life should be classified as murder. Only modern genetics seems to lead to that conclusion, with its teaching about the unrepeatability or at least the never-to-be-repeated character of that first informational speck each of us once was and still is in every cell and attribute. Theology, however, is premicrobiology! The theologians debate the question, *when* between conception and birth the unique not-to-be-repeated individual human being has arrived on the scene. Wherever the line is drawn, the direct destruction of a fetus after that point will, by definition, be murder, while before that point its direct destruction would fall under some other species of sin or grave violation.

In the prenatal development of the fetus, "animation" is the point between conception and birth that is usually taken to be crucial, although as we shall see animation may have more than one meaning. If animation and not impregnation

65

or birth is the moment when an individual offspring first begins to be what he is to become and launches on a course of thereafter becoming what he already is, then direct abortion after animation would be to kill a man alive. It would be—morally, not legally—a species of murder. Then, on this view, to define direct abortion before animation as an offense would require that such an action be understood to fall within a class of less serious violations. In no case would the destruction of a preanimate fetus raise questions regarding the respect due or the rights and sanctity of another distinct human life. The fetus is then not yet human; it is still only a part of the mother's body, even though there may be a special responsibility for this prehuman material out of which is to come, at animation, a man alive.

The term "animation" may be understood in two different ways, and from this follows two different views concerning when in the course of the development of a fetus its direct abortion would be murder. "Animation" may most obviously be taken to indicate the moment fetal life becomes an independent source of movement in the womb, and modern thought would define animation in terms of physical motion. This should perhaps be called "quickening," the better to distinguish it from the second, the classical and more philosophical interpretation.

It was once commonly believed that there were forty days for the male and eighty days for the female between impregnation and the time, long before quickening, when the fetus became animate in this other sense. The second and more fundamental meaning of "animation" is derived not from motion but from *anima* (soul). The controlling philosophical doctrine was one which held that the soul is the *form* of the body. Thus *fetus animatus* = *fetus humanus* = *fetus formatus*. This did not entail another purely physical determination of when there was a formed fetus, or a fetus in human form or shape, on the scene. That would be earlier, of course, than when the fetus quickens. The meaning of the soul as the form of the body was too subtle a notion for that. It entailed a belief that there is a living human fetus, possibly much earlier than when there is either discernible motion or discernible human shape.

But the point to be noted here is that in theoretical speculation there has never been a certain or unanimous opinion among theologians to the effect that a *fetus humanus/fetus animatus* begins to be at the very moment of conception. In the controversies among theologians past and present, there has always been allowed a period of time between conception and "animation." "Scientifically" or at the level of theory or doctrine, one cannot speak with certainty of a human fetus before the lapse, some say, of six days.[2] It is the modern science

[2] Many of the themes and distinctions in the text above are exhibited in the remarks of a much-used commentary on the Code of Canon Law of 1917, specifically upon Canon 985, in reference to actions which after baptism would incur for a man "irregularity by delict" and render him unworthy of entering the clerical state or of exercising the orders he may have already received. The paragraph is as follows:

Those who perform an abortion on a human being incur irregularity, provided, of course, the act is committed, not accidentally or unawares, but intentionally or through grievous culpability, even though by accident. The aborted fetus must be a *fetus humanus*,

of genetics and not theology that theoretically closes this gap completely (unless *blastocyst* in the case of identical twins is taken to be some sort of *rebutting* scientific evidence for identifying the moment of animation).

In any case, the older theologians distinguished between a formed fetus and a quickened fetus, and between nutritive, animal, and intellectual parts of the soul. They did not go so far as to say that all this was created and infused at impregnation. By the intellectual or human soul informing the fetus and by the doctrine that the soul is the "form" of the body, they meant an immanent constitutive element, not "form" in the sense of physical shape. Their reasoning entailed a dis-

---

and, as is generally added, *animatus*, i.e. a living human fetus. We were surprised to see no reference, among Card. Gasparri's quotations, to the Constitution of Gregory XIV, "*Sedes Apostolica*," of May 31, 1591, which restricted irregularity and penalties to the *fetus animatus*, as the old law had it. However, said Constitution is quoted under can. 2350, §1. We believe that the unanimous teaching of the school should not be set aside, especially since the wording *fetus humanus* can only signify a living fetus. Animation, as stated before, takes place within the first week after conception. Theologians as well as canonists admit that the old theory concerning animation may still be held as far as the incurring of penalties and irregularities is concerned. This theory is that between the conception and the animation of a male fetus forty days, and of a female fetus, eighty days elapse. As long as no authentic declaration has been issued, the strict interpretation applied to penal laws may be followed here, and the period of forty, respectively eighty days be admitted. At any rate, we cannot scientifically speak of a human fetus before the lapse of six days after conception.
Roger John Huser, *The Crime of Abortion in Canon Law* (Washington, D.C.: Catholic University of America, 1942), quoted by Eugene Quay, "Justifiable Abortion," *Georgetown Law Journal*, XLIX, No. 3 (Spring, 1961), 438.

tinction between *fetus formatus/fetus animatus* and a quickened fetus. This meant, of course, that the embryo became essentially human very early in its development—much earlier than could be concluded from form or animation in the gross physical senses of these terms.

In a remarkable way, modern genetics also teaches that there are "formal causes," immanent principles, or constitutive elements long before there is any shape or motion or discernible size. These minute formal elements are already determining the organic life to be the uniquely individual human being it is to be. According to this present-day scientific equivalent of the doctrine that the soul is the "form" or immanent *entelechy* of the body, it can now be asserted for the first time in the history of "scientific" speculation upon this question that who one is and is to be is present from the moment the ovum is impregnated.

One can, of course, allow this and still refuse to affirm that the embryo is as yet in any sense the bearer of human rights. In that case, however, one would have to provide himself with some account (perhaps drawn from these ancient and contemporary accounts of the prenatal and postnatal development of human personhood) of how by stages or degrees a human offspring approaches sacredness, and he would have to say when a child probably attains life that has sanctity. One could, for example, take "viability" and not impregnation or animation or quickening or actual birth as the point in time when the fetus becomes subject to the protections due to any human life. Glanville Williams has recently proposed another place to draw the line, this time in between quickening and viability. "One might take," he writes, "the time at which the fetal brain begins to function," which can be determined by electrodes detecting the electric potentials or "brain waves" that are discernible in the seventh month or shortly before the time of viability, to be the beginning of justifiable protection for the fetus.[3]

Of all these demarcations, the time of birth would in many ways seem the least likely account of the beginning of life that has dignity and sanctity. A newborn baby is not noticeably much more human than before. It can, of course, do its own breathing; but, before it could within limits do its own moving, and it could very definitely do its own dying. While its independence of its mother's body is relatively greater, even dramatically greater, a born baby is still a long, long way from being able to do its own praying, from being a "subject," an "I," or from being rational.

Having begun with all these distinctions and theories about when germinating life becomes human, it is now necessary for me to say that from an authentic religious point of view none of them matters very much.

Strictly speaking, it is far more crucial for contemporary thought than it is for any religious viewpoint to *say when* there is on the scene enough of the actuality of a man who is coming to be for there to be any sacredness in or any rights

[3] Glanville Williams, *The Sanctity of Life and the Criminal Law* (New York: Alfred A. Knopf, 1957), p. 231.

attached to his life. For in modern world views, the sanctity of life could rest only on something inherent in man. It is, therefore, important to determine when proleptically he already essentially is all else that he will ever become in the course of a long life. The sanctity of life in the first of it, if this has any sacredness, must be an overflow backward from or in anticipation of something—some capability or power—that comes later to be a man's inherent possession.

One grasps the religious outlook upon the sanctity of human life only if he sees that this life is asserted to be *surrounded* by sanctity that need not be in a man; that the most dignity a man ever possesses is a dignity that is alien to him. From this point of view it becomes *relatively* unimportant to say exactly when among the products of human generation we are dealing with an organism that is human and when we are dealing with organic life that is not yet human (despite all the theological speculations upon this question). A man's dignity is an overflow from God's dealings with him, and not primarily an anticipation of anything he will ever be by himself alone.

This is why in our religious traditions fetal life was *so certainly* surrounded with protections and prohibitions. This is why fetal life was surrounded by protections for the time before anyone supposed that a "man alive" assuredly existed, and even when, in opinions then current, there was a great degree of probability that he did not. "When nature is in deliberation about the man," [4] Christians through the ages knew

[4] Tertullian *Apologia* ix. 6–7.

71

that God was in deliberation about the man. This took some of the weight off of analyzing the stages in the course of nature's deliberations, and off of the proofs from nature and from reason that were nevertheless used.

The value of a human life is ultimately grounded in the value God is placing on it. Anyone who can himself stand imaginatively even for a moment within an outlook where everything is referred finally to God—who, from things that are not, brings into being the things that are—should be able to see that God's deliberations about the man need have only begun. If there is anything incredible here, it is not the science, but the pitch of faith which no science proves, disproves, or confirms.

According to the religious outlooks and "on-looks" that have been traditional to us, man is a sacredness *in* human biological processes no less than he is a sacredness in the human social or political order. That sacredness is not composed by observable degrees of relative worth. A life's sanctity consists not in its worth *to* anybody. What life is in and of itself is most clearly to be seen in situations of naked equality of one life with another, and in the situation of congeneric helplessness which is the human condition in the first of life. No one is ever much more than a fellow fetus; and in order not to become confused about life's primary value, it is best not to concentrate on degrees of relative worth we may later acquire.

The Lord did not set his love upon you, nor choose you, because you were already intrinsically more than a blob of tissue in the uterus or greater in size than the period at the end of this sentence. Even so, the writer of Deuteronomy proclaimed to the children of Israel:

> The Lord did not set his love upon you, nor choose you, because you were more in number than any people; for you were the fewest of all people.
> But because the Lord loved you, and because he would keep the oath which he had sworn unto your fathers, hath the Lord brought you out with a mighty hand . . . [7:7, 8a].

Not only the prophet Jeremiah, but anyone who has a glimmer of what it means to be a religious man, should be able to repeat after him: "Before I formed thee in the belly I knew thee; and before thou camest forth out of the womb I sanctified thee; and I ordained thee . . ." (1:5). Or after the Psalmist:

> O Lord, thou hast searched me, and known me.
> . . . .
> Thou has beset me behind and before, and laid thy hand upon me.
> . . . .
> Behold . . . the darkness and the light are both alike to thee.
> For thou hast possessed my reins:
> Thou hast covered me in my mother's womb.
> I will praise thee; for I am fearfully and wonderfully made: Marvelous are thy works: and that my soul knoweth right well [139:1, 5, 12b, 13, 14].

Thus, every human being is a unique, unrepeatable opportunity to praise God. His life is entirely an ordination, a loan, and a stewardship. His essence is his existence before God and to God, as it is from Him. His dignity is "an *alien* dig-

73

nity," an evaluation that is not of him but placed upon him by the divine decree.

In regard to the respect to be accorded this generic, nascent, and dying life of ours, it does not matter much which of several religious formulations is chiefly invoked. This may be the doctrine concerning the origin of a human life, or man's creation in the image of God. It may be the biblical doctrine of God's covenant with his people and thence with all mankind, with the standard this provides for the mercy to be extended in every human relation. It may be the doctrine concerning man's ultimate destination. Nor does it matter much whether it is man's life from God, before God, or toward God that is most stressed in a religious philosophy of life, whether it is supernatural faith or divine charity or supernatural hope that bestows the value. In all cases it is hardly possible to exclude what is nowadays narrowly called "nascent life" from our purview or from the blessing and sanctity and protection which—a religious man is convinced—God places over all human lives. *Sub specie Dei* human procreation is pro-creation. That is the most fundamental "pro" word in our vocabulary. This means procreation in God's behalf. *Sub specie Dei*, it was not because it could be proved that after a certain point in our pre- or even our postnatal development we became discernibly "human" and thus a bearer of rights and deserving of respect, while before that we were not; it was rather because the Lord loved us even while we were yet microscopic and sent forth his call upon us and brought forth from things that are not the things that are. *Sub specie Dei*, it is precisely the

little ones who have hardly any human claims who are sought
out and covered by his mercy. *Sub specie Dei*, it is precisely
when all reasonable natural grounds for hope are gone that
one needs hope and may hope in God, even as when all hope
was gone Abraham hoped on in faith; and in this perspective
it is hardly possible to exclude from the meaning of nascent
life God's call sent forth among men that once again they
have hope beyond and beneath the limits reason might
set.

These Biblical themes resound throughout Karl Barth's
writings on respect for life and the protection of life. For the
greatest Protestant theologian of this generation, the congeneric human situation is that ours is a "fellow humanity"
held in trust. Respect for life means that a man should "treat
as a loan both the life of all men with his own and his own
with that of all men." [5] "Respect" is indeed too pale a term to
use for the attitude and response of those who "handle life as
a divine loan" (p. 338). Or rather—since Barth uses the
term—we must allow the word "respect" to be filled full of
the meaning and awe derived from the fact that whenever a
man's life is in question the primary affirmation to be made
about it is that from all eternity God resolved not even to be
God without this particular human life.

Respect is man's astonishment, humility and awe at a fact in which
he meets something superior—majesty, dignity, holiness, a mystery

[5] Karl Barth, *Church Dogmatics* (Edinburg: T. and T. Clark, 1961),
Vol. III/4, para. 55, p. 335. All parenthetical references in the text are
to this work.

which compels him to withdraw and keep his distance, to handle it modestly, circumspectly and carefully. . . . When man in faith in God's Word and promise realizes how God from eternity has maintained and loved him in his little life, and what He has done for him in time, in this knowledge of human life he is faced by a majestic, dignified and holy fact. In human life itself he meets something superior. . . . [The incarnation of Jesus Christ, the Word of God made *man*] unmistakeably differentiates human life from everything that is and is done in heaven and earth. This gives it even in its most doubtful form the character of something singular, unique, unrepeatable and irreplaceable. This decides that it is an advantage and something worthwhile to be as man. This characterizes life as the incomparable and non-recurrent opportunity to praise God [p. *339*].

Respect means to treat human life with "holy awe" (p. *344*).

Respect for life does not mean that a man must live and let live from some iron law of necessity, or even that there is a rational compulsion to do this, or a decisive rational ground for doing so. It is rather that because God has said "Yes" to life, man's "Yes" should echo His. First and foremost, this means that man can and may live; he can and may respect the lives of others with his own. Into the darkness of the void before creation, or of the suicide's despair, or of a woman's womb, went forth the Divine utterance, "Thou mayest live." Because of God's decree and election, a man, in his own case, can and may live; he should ("must") accept his life as a trust superior to his own determination. Because the "can" and "may" that went forth also to summon every other life together with his own came from the same God and not from any human source, he can and may and must say the only human word that is appropriate or in accord with God's Yea-saying: "Thou, too, mayest live."

It is obviously because of this understanding of the meaning of life's sanctity that Barth can write, as it were, from above about nascent life, and not because of some pseudo science or even a correct science describing prenatal life from the under-side:

The unborn child is from the very first a child. It is still developing and has no independent life. But it is a man and not a thing, nor a mere part of the mother's body. . . . He who destroys germinating life kills a man and thus ventures the monstrous thing of decreeing concerning the life and death of a fellow-man whose life is given by God and therefore, like his own, belongs to Him [pp. 415–16].

It is precisely because *it is only nascent* life, weak and helpless and with no intrinsic reason for claiming anything by inherent right, that Barth can say: "This child is a man for whose life the Son of God has died. . . . The true light of the world shines already in the darkness of the mother's womb" (p. 416). Or again: "Those who live by mercy will always be disposed to practice mercy, especially to a human being which is so dependent on the mercy of others as the unborn child" (p. 418).

Because it is the Lord who has beset him behind and before, the child is a bit of sacredness in the temporal and biological order—whether it is in the womb of the mother, in the arms of its father, playing hopscotch on the sidewalk, a profes-

77

sional football player, or a scientist at work in his laboratory (or whichever one you value most). Each has the same title to life immediately from God.

Nothing in the foregoing solves any problems. In these meager times, it is first necessary to create the problem; and this, I venture to believe, is more important than solutions to the problem—namely, the problems arising from the sanctity of life in the first of it.

Nevertheless, by endorsing a religious understanding of the sanctity of nascent life, I have made myself responsible for offering some minimal comment upon the direction and the ingredients of actual moral decisions in the matter of abortion.

1. Roman Catholic theologians do *not* in principle teach that absolute preference is to be given to the child's life over that of the mother in cases of fatal conflict between them. This may seem to be the case in practice only because of an extraordinary effort to do nothing that denies them *equal* rights and *equal* protection. Protestant Christians and everyone of whatever profound religious outlook must join the Roman Catholics in experiencing extraordinary anguish in the face of situations that throw life against nascent life, each of whom has *equal* title to protection.

My first comment is that we must adopt the main "rule of practice," which Roman Catholicism unfolds for the charitable protection of human life in cases of irremediable conflict of equals. This is the distinction between *direct* and *indirect* abortion. To abort the fetus may be the foreknown, anticipated, and permitted result of surgical or other emergency action whose *primary thrust* is directed to the end of saving the mother's life. An action may in its *primary thrust* be to save the mother's life, while it is foreknown that the fetus will or will likely die or be killed in the course of thus giving medical attention to the mother; or, if the fetus is viable, the primary thrust of the medical action may be to save the nascent life, while it is foreknown that the mother will or will likely die or be killed as a secondary consequence of trying to save her child's life. My language distinguishing between the primary and the secondary *thrust* of an action may be a peculiar Americanism. If so, it has to be invented in these times and among Protestants who have so far reduced the meaning of "the intention of an act" that it has come to mean only the motives of the agent. Today we seem able to analyze play acting better than we can analyze moral action, in that we can distinguish the "intention" of a drama from the motives and meaning the author may have had in mind, but are scarcely able to grasp the fact that the intention of moral action is not exactly the same as the subjective motives of the man who is the agent. (These, too, should be righteous.)

It is in these terms that Catholics distinguish between direct and indirect, intended and unintended, abortion. The latter can be justified but the former cannot; and, of course, neither death should be subjectively *wanted*. This rule of moral practice seems to be both a logical and a charitable extension of ethical deliberations impelled by respect for the *equal* sanctity of both the lives that are in mortal conflict, and both of whom one wants to save.

2. My second comment addresses cases that cannot be covered by the justification of indirect abortion only. The conflict situation may be one in which the mother's life cannot be saved and both will die unless the main thrust of the medical action is to kill the fetus. I do not know how many *sorts* of birth-room emergencies fall under this classification. I suspect there are fewer of this *kind* or of these *kinds* of cases than is ordinarily supposed by persons who do not know Roman Catholic medical ethics, and therefore do not know how far this has gone in resolving one type of case after another (including ectopic pregnancy) so as to permit the action to be taken that alone will save the one life that can be saved while allowing the fetus to die. Nor do I know how often unique, individual cases may arise, even under *kinds* of medical difficulties where ordinarily indirect abortion will save the mother's life, in which a conscientious physician must judge that, taking everything into account, more positive and direct action must be taken in *this* situation or else both will die. I suspect that the number of instances in which medical practice limited to indirect abortion would be a law that kills, or rather one that allows both to die, is greater than Roman Catholic moralists suppose.

It seems altogether likely, however, whether by reason of some critical *kind* or *kinds* of medical situations or by reason of unique situations falling under any of these kinds in all their individual features, that there is need for taking up the question of the possible justification of *direct* abortion in cases of mortal conflict between a mother's life and a nascent life where only the mother can be saved. In cases in which both will die together unless the mother's life is saved by an act of direct abortion, does the person who secures or performs this operation do something *wrong* that good may come of it?

I think not. This would be to do the *right* thing as means (where no other means are available), and not only to seek a good end. It is permissible, nay, it is even morally obligatory to kill the fetus directly if, without this, both mother and child will die together.

The usual arguments for this practice, however, are quite inadequate. There needs to be Christian, rational, moral reflection penetrating the act of justifiable direct abortion itself, and not only its justifying circumstances or good results. In particular, if we are serious about ethics, the Protestant Christian should wrestle with his Catholic brother over the verdict each delivers upon this proposed action in the course of his deliberations upon the Christian moral life. It is not sufficient for the Protestant simply to *assert* arbitrarily that direct abortion is the right action to be performed, and then fix his attention on the results of such conduct, on the life that is saved by this means. The goodness of this result was never in question. No one doubts that the action in question respects the sanctity of the mother's life. The question that was raised, and the question each Christian must face, is whether direct abortion is not in every way incompatible with any remaining regard for the sanctity of the nascent life.

What can and may and must be said about direct abortion insofar as this is an action brought upon the child? If Roman Catholicism is incorrect in prohibiting this as a choice-worthy means for saving the mother's life (which is only of *equal* value), then it must be possible for ethical reflection to penetrate the action proposed for situations of mortal conflict in a fashion that is, morally, significantly distinguishable from the Catholic moral penetration of it. It helps not at all to say that we should do what love requires in the consequences, since the question was whether every shred of respect for the sanctity of nascent life must not be abandoned ever to do such a thing *to the child* for the sake of those consequences. No one ever doubted that the proposed action in its effects would be charitable to the mother. It is therefore no argument to say that it is.

The first thing that should be said concerning a forced choice of justifiable direct abortion is that the *motives* of the agent toward the child should not be any different from his motives toward the mother's life. To want to save her, it is not necessary for him to *want* the death of the fetus. In fact, the death of the fetus can and should be radically *unwanted*. A person should perform or procure a direct abortion in the midst of a mortal conflict of life with life, while not *wanting* the death of either. To this degree and in the motivational realm, a person does not altogether deny the equality of these two lives to God, or direct his own human love upon the one and not the other.

If it is objected that the fetus will be dead anyway, and

moreover by an act of direct aggression on his life, the answer has to be that the motives of moral agents constitute a part, if only a part, of the meaning of righteousness, along with the intention and direction of action, the consequences, and so forth. It should also be said that the requirement that in the agent's *motives* the death of the fetus be never *wanted* (which I grant has no practical consequence in the case of direct abortion to save the mother's life) may be among the *deciding* factors in assessing proposals that abortion is justifiable under other circumstances. Just so, the distinction between direct and indirect abortion, between killing and allowing to die, has no practical consequences at all in cases in which medically it is possible to save the one life that can be saved only by direct action. Still, ethical deliberation must traverse this ground and clarify this distinction, if for no other reason than that it is likely to prove to be among the deciding factors or to be definitive of the action to be adopted in other cases or circumstances.

Having said this about the moral agent's not *wanting* motivationally the death of the child which he encompasses, one has then to ask if anything more can be said about justifiable direct abortion. Can *the action itself* and *its intention* be further penetrated by Christian moral reflection, and not only the heart of the moral agent? Certainly, if there is more to be said, this should be traced out.

We must side with Karl Barth [6] against reducing ethics to motivation alone, and much more against reducing it to moti-

[6] *Ibid.*, p. 425.

vations that have in regard only the mother's life and have already put empty room in the place of nascent life.

As regards the intentionality and the direction of the act of direct abortion which we are discussing, this much more must be said. The intention of the action, and in this sense its direction, is not upon the *death* of the fetus, any more than are the motives of the agent. The intention of the action is directed toward the *incapacitation* of the fetus from doing what it is doing to the life of the mother, and is not directed toward the death of the fetus, as such, even in the killing of it. The child, of course, is only doing what comes naturally, i.e., growing and attempting to be born. But this, objectively and materially, is aggressing upon the life of its mother. Her life, which alone can be saved, can be saved only if this is stopped; and to incapacitate the fetus from doing this can be done only, we are supposing, by a direct act of killing nascent life. Still, in this situation it is correct to say that the intention of this action is not the killing, not the death of the fetus, but the incapacitation of it from carrying out the material aggression that it is effecting upon the life of the mother.

This is the way that the Protestant Christian should wrestle with his fellow Catholic moralist for the verdict approving direct abortion as a means. Of course, the child is innocent; it is not "formally" or deliberately and culpably an aggressor. It is, however, a most unchristian line of reasoning that makes so much of a distinction between guilt and innocence in measuring out sanctity and respect to life. If this is true, then finding a guilty one cannot be the basic justification for ever

84

killing a man. Catholicism simply stakes too much on an autonomous natural justice in every one of its judgments about when a formally guilty aggressor forfeits his right to life (and the same applies to everything said about the fact that the fetus has done nothing to forfeit its right to life). The determination of right conduct simply should not stop at the distinction between the "innocent" and the "aggressor," if our reflection upon righteousness has in any significant measure been invaded by the righteousness of God, who makes rain to fall upon the just and the unjust and has surrounded not only microscopic life but also ungodly lives with sanctity and protection.

We must argue, therefore, that precisely the fact and the effects of *material* aggression of life upon life should be the main concern in our attempts to penetrate the meaning of the Christian life, not waiting to find a guilty aggressor before we are permitted ever to take one life in order to save another in a mortal conflict of lives and values. Just so, in warfare it is not guilty aggressors but material aggression that ever warrants the taking of life to stop the action that is going on. Moreover, a proper analysis of the intentionality and direction of an act of war in killing an enemy soldier is exactly that proposed here in the case of justifiable abortion. It is the incapacitation of the soldier and not his death that is the intention of the action.[7] If a combatant surrenders and inca-

---

[7] No less an authority than Thomas Aquinas can be cited in support of this analysis of an act of justifiable killing, in his original formulation of the rule of "double effect" (*Summa Theologica*, II-II, Q. 64,

pacitates himself, the just and the actual objective in ever killing him has been secured; and nothing would then justify his death. The fact that he, as materially the bearer of the force that should be stopped, cannot otherwise be incapacitated than by death or surrender is the tragedy of war. The fact that the nascent life cannot incapacitate itself from materially bearing its force against the only life that can be saved, in the case we are supposing, is the tragedy of abortion. But in neither case is wickedness done. These actions are not *morally* evil, either in the motives of the agent or in the intention of the action, because the agent need not *want* the death of another human being nor by his action does he *intend* this. He wants and his action intends rather the incapacitation of a life that is exerting materially aggressive fatal force upon the life of another. The stopping of materially aggressive action is the highest possible warrant for the killing of men by men (if life cannot otherwise be saved), not the aggressor-innocent distinction.

3. My final comment concerns the principal value to be derived from steadfastly maintaining the verdicts that can be reached in ethical justification or prohibition from a religious understanding of the sanctity of life and also of nascent life. This is not always or primarily the praise or blame of individual actions or agents. These may, for a variety of reasons, be *excusable* even for wrongdoing, and the judgment of blameworthiness may fall elsewhere, e.g., upon the moral

---

art. 7). After much derision of Catholic moral analysis, Glanville Williams makes this same point in *The Sanctity of Life*, p. 204.

ethos of an entire society or epoch. We need, therefore, to look to the fundamental moral premises of contemporary society in order to see clearly what is at stake in the survival or demise of a religious evaluation of nascent life.

This is an abortifacient society. Women readily learn to "loop before you leap," but they forget to ask whether interuterine devices prevent conception or abort germinating life. They do both. A significant part of the efficiency of the loop arises from the fact that it is not only a contraceptive, but also an abortifacient. The pills that prevent ovulation are more totally effective than the combined capacities of the loop, and this fact alone in an abortifacient civilization will lead to preference for the pill in the practice of birth control.

American women who can afford to do so go to Sweden to avail themselves of more liberal legal regulations concerning abortion; but Swedish women go to Poland, which is at the moment the real paradise for legal abortions. Sweden's is a middle way between American rigidity and Polish unlimited permissiveness. The stated reason why Sweden does not go further and adopt still more liberal practices in regard to legal abortion is because of the fear that, as one doctor put it, where abortion is altogether easy, people will not take care to practice birth control.[8] Abortion is therefore a contraceptive device in this age. Doubtless, it is not the most choice-worthy means or a means frequently chosen, but it is an alternative means. Loop before you leap, abort before you birth! The evidence seems to be that the latter may not be merely a last

[8] "Abortion and the Law," *CBS Reports*, April 5, 1965.

87

resort, but is actually an option for contraceptive purposes. If quite freely available, abortion may relieve the moral and psychological pressures that are exerted upon their freedom to copulate by the remaining regard that men and women have for possible nascent life. Just as surely as this is a contraceptive society, it is also abortifacient.

We are not concerned here with what the criminal law should be in regard to abortion. Not everything that is legal is right, nor should every wrong be legally prohibited; and nothing that is right is right *because* it is legal. Perhaps the penal code regarding abortion should be reformed in directions that will lead to less evil being done than is done under our present more stringent laws.[9] However, in comprehending the meaning of describing this age as an abortifacient civilization (in contrast to societies based at all on religious comprehension of the sanctity of life), it is illuminating to notice what happens when legal prohibitions of abortion are "liberalized." Glanville Williams [10] has this to say about the Swedish experiment: "There is convincing evidence that it is to a large extent an entirely new clientele that is now granted legal abortion, that is to say women who would not have had an illegal abortion if they had been refused the legal one." Thereupon Williams states and endorses the value

[9] Note that I say, "lead to less evil being done than is *done*," not "to less evil *happening* than now occurs." This is to say that a primary legislative purpose of law and of the reform of law in this area should remain a moral one. The goal of law is the regulation of human *conduct*, and not only the prevention of certain consequences.

[10] Williams, *The Sanctity of Life*, p. 242.

judgment upon these abortifacient trends that are characteristic of the contemporary period: "Although the social result is rather to add the total of legal abortions to the total of illegal abortions than to reduce the number of illegal abortions, a body of medical opinion refuses to regret the legal abortions on this account." That judgment is, of course, in no sense a "medical opinion."

The foregoing analysis of our society as in its ethos abortifacient is pertinent to the question concerning the moral justification of (direct) abortion of a fetus that is likely to be gravely defective physically or mentally. The answer to this question seems obvious indeed to a simple and sincere humanitarianism. It is not at all obvious. A first step in throwing doubt upon the proposal is to ask what was forgotten in the discussion of the blindness and deformities that will result from a woman's contracting rubella, especially in early pregnancy. It is often hard to tell whether a woman has rubella; yet her child may be gravely damaged. Moreover, it is hard to tell whether an individual case of measles is rubella; this can be determined with a great degree of certainty only in the case of *epidemics* of rubella. It is proposed that women who have rubella while pregnant should be able to secure a legal abortion, and it is affirmed that under these circumstances fetal euthanasia is not only ethically permissible but may even be morally obligatory for the sake of the child.

We are interested primarily in the ethical question. The proposal, as I understand it, is based on a kind of *interims ethik;* direct abortion is justified at least until medical science

89

develops a *vaccine* against these measles and a reliable *test* of whether a woman has or has had the German measles. In our abortifacient culture, however, it is forgotten, or if mentioned it does not sink into the consciousness of men and women today, that there is an alternative to adopting the widespread medical practice and legal institution of fetal euthanasia. This optional social practice of medicine would be equally or more preventive of damage to nascent life from rubella. The *disease itself* gives complete immunization to contracting rubella again. The popular belief that a woman can have several cases of German measles is an "old wives' tale," my pediatrician tells me, which arises from the fact that it is almost impossible to tell one sort of measles from another, except in epidemics. But there is one way to be certain of this, and to obtain immunization against the disease in the future. The virus itself, the disease itself, can be used, as it were, to "vaccinate" against itself.

Why is it not proposed that for the interim between now and the perfection of a more convenient, reliable vaccine, all girl children be *given* the German measles? [11] Would this not be a more choice-worthy *interims ethik?* The answer to this question can only be found in the complete erosion of religious regard for nascent life in a technological and abortifacient era. Abortion when the mother contracts rubella is another

---

[11] There are sometimes, of course, serious effects from having German measles. Still, it is arguable that these effects would be far less serious than the destruction of both damaged and undamaged nascent lives which, it is said, ought now systematically to be inflicted while we await the perfection and widespread use of a vaccine.

example of the "American way of death." In this instance, the darkness of the womb makes unnecessary resort to a mortician's art to cover the grim reality. As long as we do not see the deaths inflicted or witness the dying, the direct killing of nascent life has only to be compared with the greater or less inconvenience of other solutions in an antiseptic society where the prevention of disease at all cost is the chief light upon our conscious paths. But that darkness and this light are both alike to the Lord of nascent and conscious life. Upon this basis it is not possible to choose actions and practices that deliberately abort over an interim social practice of deliberate disease giving. At least in the problem of rubella-induced fetal damage, it is not mercy or charity but some other motivation in regard to sentient life that can look with favor upon the practice of euthanasia for the child's sake.

The real situation in which our ethical deliberations should proceed cannot be adequately defined short of the location of moral agency and the action under consideration in the context of the lives of all mankind and the general social practices most apt to exhibit righteousness or to make for good. Moreover, our ethical deliberations cannot disregard the fact that the *specific* contemporary context must include the erosion of the moral bond between moments in a single individual life without which there can be no enduring covenants of life with life—the erosion of the moral bonds between life and life, between soul and bodily life, and between conscious life and nascent life—which has brought about the divorcing,

91

contraceptive, and abortifacient ethos of the present day.

A chief business of ethics is to distinguish between venereal freedom and the meaning of venereal responsibility in such a fashion that it is barely possible (or at least that this possibility is not methodologically excluded) that from the reflections of moralists there may come clear direction for the structural changes needed to address the structural defects of this age. If this is so, I suggest that a strong case can be made for every effort to revitalize a religious understanding of the integrity and sanctity of life, for unfolding from this at the outmost limits the distinction between direct killing and allowing to die and the distinction between intending to kill and intending to incapacitate the fetus to save the mother's life, and for retaining in the order of ethical justification the prohibition of the direct killing of nascent life. This would be to keep needed moral pressures upon ourselves in many areas where a proper regard for life threatens to be dissolved, or has already been dissolved. This would be to endeavor to reverse the trends of a scientific and a secular age that have already gone far in emptying our culture of any substantive morality.

The first order of business would be to strengthen an ethics that contains some remaining sense of the sanctity of life against the corrosive influence of the view that what *should* be done is largely a function of what *technically can* be done, and against the view that morality is entirely a matter of engineering the consequences for the conscious span of our lives. Moreover, if we do not confuse ethical justification with moral excusability, compassion can still encompass the possibility and the reality of individual moral excusability for a wrong that had to be done or was done in a particular situation in this world where sin (especially the sin in social structures) begets sin.

Genetic Options:
An Examination of Current Fallacies

I DO NOT intend to deny that the advances of science may sometimes have consequences that endanger, if not life itself, then the quality of life or our self-respect as human beings (for it is in this wider sense that I think "sanctity" should be construed). Nor shall I waste time by defending science as a whole or scientists generally against a charge of inner or essential malevolence. The Wicked Scientist is not to be taken seriously: Dr. Strangelove, Dr. Moreau, Dr. Moriarty, Dr. Mabuse, Dr. Frankenstein (an honorary degree, this), and the rest of them are puppets of Gothic fiction. Scientists, on the whole, are amiable and well-meaning creatures. There must be very few wicked scientists. There are, however, plenty of wicked philosophers, wicked priests, and wicked politicians.

One of the gravest charges ever made against science is

P. B. MEDAWAR

that biology has now put it into our power to corrupt both the body and the mind of man. By scientific means (the charge runs) we can now breed different kinds and different races—different models, almost—of human beings, degrading some, making aristocrats of others, adapting others still to special purposes: treating them in fact like dogs, for this is how we *have* treated dogs. Or again: science now makes it possible to dominate and control the thought of human beings—to improve them, perhaps, if that should be our purpose, but more often to enslave or to corrupt with evil teaching.

But these things have always been possible. At any time in the past five thousand years it would have been within our power to embark on a program of selecting and culling human beings and raising breeds as different from one another as toy poodles and Pekingese are from St. Bernards and

95

Great Danes. In a genetic sense the empirical arts of the breeder are just as applicable to human beings as to horses— more easily applicable, in fact, for human beings are highly *evolvable* animals, a property they owe partly to an open and uncomplicated breeding system, which allows them a glorious range of inborn diversity and therefore a tremendous evolutionary potential; and partly to their lack of physical specializations (in the sense in which anteaters and woodpeckers and indeed dogs are specialized), a property which gives human beings a sort of amateur status among animals. And it has always been possible to pervert or corrupt human beings by coercion, propaganda, or evil indoctrination. Science has not yet improved these methods, nor have scientists used them. They have, however, been used to great effect by politicians, philosophers, and priests.

The mischief that science may do grows just as often out of trying to do good—as, for example, improving the yield of soil is intended to do good—as out of actions intended to be destructive. The reason is simple enough: however hard we try, we do not and sometimes cannot foresee all the distant consequences of scientific innovation. No one clearly foresaw that the widespread use of antibiotics might bring about an evolution of organisms resistant to their action. No one could have predicted that X-irradiation was a possible cause of cancer. No one could have foreseen the speed and scale with which advances in medicine and public health would create a problem of overpopulation that threatens to undo much of what medical science has worked for. (Thirty years ago the talk was all of how the people of the Western world were reproducing themselves too slowly to make good the wastage of mortality; we heard tell of a "Twilight of Parenthood," and wondered rather fearfully where it all would end.) But somehow or other we shall get round all these problems, for every one of them is soluble, even the population problem, and even though its solution is obstructed above all else by the bigotry of some of our fellow men.

I choose from medicine and medical biology one or two concrete examples of how advances in science threaten or seem to threaten the sanctity of human life. Many of these threats, of course, are in no sense distinctively medical, though they are often loosely classified as such. They are merely medical contexts for far more pervasive dangers. One of them is our increasing state of dependence on medical services and the medical industries. What would become of the diabetic if the supplies of insulin dried up, or of the victims of Addison's disease deprived of synthetic steroids? Questions of this kind might be asked of every service society provides. In a complex society we all sustain and depend upon each other—for transport, communications, food, goods, shelter, protection, and a hundred other things. The medical industries will not break down all by themselves, and if they do break down it will be only one episode of a far greater disaster.

The same goes for the economic burden imposed by illness

97

in any community that takes some collective responsibility for the health of its citizens. All shared burdens have a cost which is to a greater or lesser degree shared between us: education, pensions, social welfare, legal aid, and every other social service, including government.

We are getting nearer what is distinctively medical when we ask ourselves about the economics, logistics, and morality of keeping people alive by medical intervention and medical devices. At present it is the cost and complexity of the operation, and the shortage of machines and organs, that denies a kidney graft or an artificial kidney to anyone mortally in need of it. The limiting factors are thus still economic and logistic. But what about the morality of keeping people alive by these heroic medical contrivances? I do not think it is possible to give any answer that is universally valid or that, if it were valid, would remain so for more than a very few years. Medical contrivances extend all the way from pills and plasters and bottles of tonic to complex mechanical prostheses, which will one day include mechanical hearts. At what point shall we say we are wantonly interfering with Nature and prolonging life beyond what is proper and humane?

In practice the answer we give is founded not upon abstract moralizing but upon a certain natural sense of the fitness of things, a feeling that is shared by most kind and reasonable people even if we cannot define it in philosophically defensible or legally accountable terms. It is only at international conferences that we tend to adopt the convention that people behave like idiots unless acting upon clear and well-turned instructions to behave sensibly. There is in fact no general formula or smooth form of words we can appeal to when in perplexity.

Moreover, our sense of what is fit and proper is not something fixed, as if it were inborn and instinctual. It changes as our experience grows, as our understanding deepens, and as we enlarge our grasp of possibilities—just as living religions and laws change, and social structures and family relationships.

I feel that our sense of what is right and just is already beginning to be offended by the idea of taking great exertions to keep alive grossly deformed or monstrous newborn children, particularly if their deformities of body or mind arise from major defects of the genetic apparatus. There are in fact scientific reasons for changing an opinion that might have seemed just and reasonable a hundred years ago.

Everybody takes it for granted, because it is so obviously true, that a married couple will have children of very different kinds and constitutions on different occasions. But the traditional opinion, which most of us are still unconsciously guided by, is that the child conceived on any one occasion is the unique and necessary product of that occasion: *that* child would have been conceived, we tend to think, or no child at all. This interpretation is quite false, but human dignity and security clamor for it. A child sometimes wonderingly acknowledges that he would never have been born at all if his mother and father had not chanced to meet and fall in love and marry. He does not realize that, instead of conceiving him, his parents might have conceived any one of a hundred thousand other children, all unlike each other and unlike himself. Only over the past one hundred years has it come to be realized that the child conceived on any one occasion belongs to a vast cohort of Possible Children, any one of whom might have been conceived and born if a different spermatozoon had chanced to fertilize the mother's egg cell—and the egg cell itself is only one of very many. It is a matter of luck then, a sort of genetic lottery. And sometimes it is cruelly bad luck—some terrible genetic conjunction, perhaps, which once in ten or twenty thousand times will bring together a matching pair of damaging recessive genes. Such a misfortune, being the outcome of a random process, is, considered in isolation, completely and essentially pointless. It is not even strictly true to say that a particular inborn abnormality must have lain within the genetic potentiality of the parents, for the malignant gene may have arisen *de novo* by mutation. The whole process is unhallowed—is, in the older sense of that word, profane.

I am saying that if we feel ourselves under a moral obligation to make every possible exertion to keep a monstrous embryo or new-born child alive *because* it is in some sense the naturally intended—and therefore the unique and privileged —product of its parents' union at the moment of its conception, then we are making an elementary and cruel blunder: for it is *luck* that determines which one child is in fact conceived out of the cohort of Possible Children that might have been conceived by those two parents on that occasion. I am not using the word "luck" of conception as such, nor of the processes of embryonic and fetal growth, nor indeed in any sense that derogates from the wonder and awe in which we hold processes of great complexity and natural beauty which we do not fully understand; I am simply using it in its proper sense and proper place.[1]

This train of thought leads me directly to eugenics—"the science," to quote its founder, Francis Galton, "which deals with all the influences that improve the inborn qualities of a race; also with those that develop them to the utmost advantage." Because the upper and lower boundaries of an individual's capability and performance are set by his genetic make-up, it is clear that if eugenic policies were to be ill-founded or mistakenly applied they could offer a most terrible threat to the sanctity and dignity of human life. This threat I shall now examine.

Eugenics is traditionally subdivided into positive and negative eugenics. Positive eugenics has to do with attempts to improve human beings by genetic policies, particularly policies founded upon selective or directed breeding. Negative eugenics has the lesser ambition of attempting to eradicate as

---

[1] There are, perhaps, weighty legal and social reasons why even tragically deformed children should be kept alive (for who is to decide? and where do we draw the line?), but these are outside my terms of reference.

many as possible of our inborn imperfections. The distinction is useful and pragmatically valid for the following reasons.[2] Defects of the genetic constitution (such as those which manifest themselves as mongolism, hemophilia, galactosemia, phenylketonuria, and a hundred other hereditary abnormalities) have a much simpler genetic basis than desirable characteristics like beauty, high physical performance, intelligence, or fertility. This is almost self-evident. All geneticists believe that "fitness" in its most general sense depends on a nicely balanced coordination and interaction of genetic factors, itself the product of laborious and long drawn out evolutionary adjustment. It is inconceivable, indeed self-contradictory, that an animal should evolve into the possession of some complex pattern of interaction between genes that made it inefficient, undesirable, or unfit—i.e., *less* well adapted to the prevailing circumstances. Likewise, a motor car will run badly for any one of a multitude of particular and special reasons, but runs well because of the harmonious mechanical interactions made possible by a sound and economically viable design.

Negative eugenics is a more manageable and understandable enterprise than positive eugenics. Nevertheless, many well-meaning people believe that, with the knowledge and skills already available to us, and within the framework of a society that upholds the rights of individuals, it is possible in principle to raise a superior kind of human being by a controlled or "recommended" scheme of mating and by regulat-

[2] See my book *The Future of Man* (New York: Basic Books, 1960).

ing the number of children each couple should be allowed or encouraged to have. If stockbreeders can do it, the argument runs, why should not we?—for who can deny that domesticated animals have been improved by deliberate human intervention?

I think this argument is unsound for a lesser and for a more important reason.

1. Domesticated animals have not been "improved" in the sense in which we should use that word of human beings. They have not enjoyed an all-round improvement, for some special characteristics or faculties have been so far as possible "fixed" without special regard to and sometimes at the expense of others. Tameness and docility are most easily achieved at the expense of intelligence, but that does not matter if what we are interested in is, say, the quality and yield of wool.

2. The ambition of the stockbreeder in the past, though he did not realize it, was twofold: not merely to achieve a predictably uniform product by artificial selection, but also to establish an internal genetic uniformity (homozygosity) in respect of the characters under selection to make sure that the stock would "breed true"—for it would be a disaster if characters selected over many generations were to be irrecoverably lost or mixed up in a hybrid progeny. The older stockbreeder believed that uniformity and breeding true were characteristics that necessarily went together, whereas we now know that they can be separately achieved. And he expected his product to fulfill two quite distinct functions which we now know to be separable, and often better separated: on the one hand, to be in themselves the favored stock and the top performers—the supersheep or supermice—and, on the other hand, to be the parents of the next generation of that stock. It is rather as if Rolls-Royces, in addition to being an end product of manufacture, had to be so designed as to give rise to Rolls-Royce progeny.

It is just as well these older views are mistaken, for with naturally outbreeding populations such as our own, genetic uniformity, arrived at and maintained by selective inbreeding, is a highly artificial state of affairs with many inherent and ineradicable disadvantages.

Stockbreeders, under genetic guidance, are now therefore inclining more and more toward a policy of deliberate and nicely calculated crossbreeding. In the simplest case, two partially inbred and internally uniform stocks are raised and perpetuated to provide two uniform lineages of parents, but the eugenic goal, the marketable end product or high performer, is the progeny of a cross between members of the two parental stocks. Being of hybrid make-up, the progeny do not breed true, and are not in fact bred from; they can be likened to a manufactured end product; but they can be uniformly reproduced at will by crossing the two parental stocks. Many more sophisticated regimens of crossbreeding have been adopted or attempted, but the innovation of principle is the same. (1) The end products are all like each other and are faithfully reproducible, but are not bred from because they do not breed true: the organisms that represent the eugenic goal have been relieved of the responsibility of reproducing themselves. And (2) the end products, though uniform in the sense of being like each other, are to a large extent hybrid—heterozygous as opposed to homozygous—in genetic composition.

The practices of stockbreeders can therefore no longer be used to support the argument that a policy of positive eugenics is applicable in principle to human beings in a society respecting the rights of individuals. The genetical manufacture of supermen by a policy of crossbreeding between two or more parental stocks is unacceptable today, and the idea that it might one day become acceptable is unacceptable also.

A deep fallacy does in fact eat into the theoretical foundations of positive eugenics and that older conception of stockbreeding out of which it grew.[3] The fallacy was to suppose that the *product* of evolution, i.e., the outcome of an episode of evolutionary change, was a new and improved genetic formula (genotype) which conferred a higher degree of adaptedness on the individuals that possessed it. This improved formula, representing a new and more successful solution of the problems of remaining alive in a hostile environment, was thought to be shared by nearly all mem-

[3] See my article "A Biological Retrospect," *Nature* (London, September 25, 1965), vol. 207, p. 1327.

bers of the newly evolved population, and to be stable except in so far as further evolution might cause it to change again. Moreover, the population would have to be predominantly homozygous in respect of the genetic factors entering into the new formula, for otherwise the individuals possessing it would not breed true to type, and everything natural selection had won would be squandered in succeeding generations.

Most geneticists think this view mistaken. It is *populations* that evolve, not the lineages and pedigrees of old-fashioned evolutionary "family trees," and the end product of an evolutionary episode is not a new genetic formula enjoyed by a group of similar individuals, but a new spectrum of genotypes, a new pattern of genetic inequality, definable only in terms of the population as a whole. Naturally out-breeding populations are not genetically uniform, even to a first approximation. They are persistently and obstinately diverse in respect of nearly all constitutional characters which have been studied deeply enough to say for certain whether they are uniform or not. It is the *population* that breeds true, not its individual members. The progeny of a given population are themselves a population with the same pattern of genetic make-up as their parents—except in so far as evolutionary or selective forces may have altered it. Nor should we think of uniformity as a desirable state of affairs which *we* can achieve even if nature, unaided, cannot. It is inherently undesirable, for a great many reasons.

The goal of positive eugenics, in its older form, cannot be achieved, and I feel that eugenic policy must be confined (paraphrasing Karl Popper) to *piecemeal genetic engineering*. That is just what negative eugenics amounts to; and now, rather than to deal in generalities, I should like to consider a concrete eugenic problem and discuss the morality of one of its possible solutions.

Some "inborn" defects—some defects that are the direct consequence of an individual's genetic make-up as it was fixed at the moment of conception—are said to be of *recessive* determination. By a recessive defect is meant one that is caused by, to put it crudely, a "bad" gene that must be present in both the gametes that unite to form a fertilized egg, i.e., in both spermatozoon and egg cell, not just in one or the other. If the bad gene *is* present in only one of the gametes, the individual that grows out of its fusion with the other is said to be a *carrier* (technically, a heterozygote).

Recessive defects are individually rather rare—their frequency is of the order of one in ten thousand—but collectively they are most important. Among them are, for example, phenylketonuria, a congenital inability to handle a certain dietary constituent, the amino acid phenylalanine, a constituent of many proteins; galactosemia, another inborn biochemical deficiency, the victims of which cannot cope metabolically with galactose, an immediate derivative of milk sugar; and, more common than either, fibrocystic disease of the pancreas, believed to be the symptom of a generalized disorder of mucus-secreting cells. All three are caused by particular single genetic defects; but their secondary consequences are manifold and deep-seated. The phenylketonuric baby is on the way to becoming an imbecile. The

107

victim of galactosemia may become blind through cataract and be mentally retarded.

Contrary to popular superstition, many congenital ailments can be prevented or, if not prevented, cured. But in this context prevention and cure have very special meanings.

The phenylketonuric or galactosemic child may be protected from the consequences of his genetic lesion by keeping him on a diet free from phenylalanine in the one case or lactose in the other. This is a most unnatural proceeding, and much easier said than done, but I take it no one would be prepared to argue that it was an unwarrantable interference with the workings of providence. It is not a cure in the usual medical sense because it neither removes nor repairs the underlying congenital deficiency. What it does is to create around the patient a special little world, a microcosm free from phenylalanine or galactose as the case may be, in which the genetic deficiency cannot express itself outwardly.

Now consider the underlying morality of prevention.

We can prevent phenylketonuria by preventing the genetic conjunction responsible for it in the first instance, i.e., by preventing the coming together of an egg cell and a sperm each carrying that same one harmful recessive gene. All but a very small proportion of overt phenylketonurics are the children of parents who are both carriers—carriers, you remember, being the people who inherited the gene from one only of the two gametes that fused at their conception. Carriers greatly outnumber the overtly afflicted. When two carriers of the same gene marry and bear children, one quarter of their children (on the average) will be normal, one quarter will be afflicted, and one half will be carriers like themselves. We shall accomplish our purpose, therefore, if, having identified the carriers—another thing easier said than done, but it *can* be done, and in an increasing number of recessive disorders—we try to discourage them *from marrying each other* by pointing out the likely consequences if they do so. The arithmetic of this is not very alarming. In a typical recessive disease, about one marriage in every five or ten thousand would be discouraged or warned against, and each disappointed party would have between fifty and a hundred other mates to choose from.

If this policy were to be carried out, the overt incidence of disease like phenylketonuria, in which carriers can be identified, would fall almost to zero between one generation and the next.

Nevertheless the first reaction to such a proposal may be one of outrage. Here is medical officiousness planning yet another insult to human dignity, yet another deprivation of the rights of man. First it was vaccination and then fluoride; if now people are not to be allowed to marry whom they please, why not make a clean job of it and overthrow the Crown or the United States Constitution?

But reflect for a moment. What is being suggested is that a certain small proportion of marriages should be discouraged for genetic reasons, to do our best to avoid bringing into the world children who are biochemically crippled. In all cultures marriages are already prohibited for genetic reasons—the prohibition, for example, of certain degrees of inbreeding (the exact degree varies from one culture or religion to another). It is difficult to see why the prohibition should have arisen to some extent independently in different cultures unless it grew out of the common observation that abnormalities are more common in the children of marriages between close relatives than in children generally. Thus the prohibition of marriage for genetic reasons has an immemorial authority behind it. As to the violation of human dignity entailed by performing tests on engaged couples that are no more complex or offensive than blood tests, let me say only this: if anyone thinks or has ever thought that religion, wealth, or color are matters that may properly be taken into account when deciding whether or not a certain marriage is a suitable one, then let him not dare to suggest that the genetic welfare of human beings should not be given equal weight.

I think that engaged couples should themselves decide, and I am pretty certain they would be guided by the thought of the welfare of their future children. When it came to be learned about twenty years ago that marriages between Rhesus-positive men and Rhesus-negative women might lead to the birth of children afflicted by hemolytic disease, a number of young couples are said to have ended their engagements—needlessly, in most cases, because the dangers were overestimated through not being understood. But that is evidence enough that young people marrying today are not likely to take stand upon some hypothetical right to give birth to defective children if, by taking thought, they can do otherwise.

The problems I have been discussing illustrate very clearly the way in which scientific evidence bears upon decisions that are not, of course, in themselves scientific. If the termination of a pregnancy is now in question, scientific evidence may tell us that the chances of a defective birth are 100 per cent, 50 per cent, 25 per cent, or perhaps unascertainable. The evidence is highly relevant to the decision, but the decision itself is not a scientific one, and I see no reason why scientists as such should be specially qualified to make it. The contribution of science is to have enlarged beyond all former bounds the evidence we must take account of before forming our opinions. Today's opinions may not be the same as yesterday's, because they are based on fuller or better evidence. We should quite often have occasion to say "I used to think that once, but now I have come to hold a rather different opinion." People who never say as much are either ineffectual or dangerous.

We all nowadays give too much thought to the material blessings or evils that science has brought with it, and too little to its power to liberate us from the confinements of ignorance and superstition.

It may be that the greatest liberation of thought ever achieved by the scientific revolution was to have given mankind the expectation of a future in this world. The idea that the world has a virtually indeterminate future is comparatively new. Much of the philosophic speculation of three hundred years ago was oppressed by the thought that the world had run its course and was coming shortly to an end.[4] "I was borne in the last age of the World," said John Donne, giving it as the "ordinarily received" opinion that the world had thrice two thousand years to run between its creation and the Second Coming. According to Archbishop Ussher's chronology more than five and a half of those six thousand years had gone by already.

No empirical evidence challenged this dark opinion. There were no new worlds to conquer, for the world was known to be spherical and therefore finite; certainly it was not all known, but the full extent of what was *not* known was known. Outer space did not put into people's minds then, as it does into ours now, the idea of a tremendous endeavor just beginning.

Moreover, life itself seemed changeless. The world a man saw about him in adult life was much the same as it had been in his own childhood, and he had no reason to think it would change in his own or his children's lifetime. We need not wonder that the promise of the next world was held out to believers as an inducement to put up with the incompleteness and inner pointlessness of this one: the present world was only a staging post on the way to better things. There was a

[4] See *The Discovery of Time*, by June Goodfield and Stephen Toulmin (New York: Macmillan, 1965).

certain awful topicality about Thomas Burnet's description of the world in flames at the end of its long journey from "a dark chaos to a bright star," for the end of the world might indeed come at any time. And Thomas Browne warned us against the folly and extravagance of raising monuments and tombs intended to last for many centuries. We are living in The Setting Part of Time, he told us: *the Great Mutations of the World are acted: it is too late to be ambitious.*

Science has now made it the ordinarily received opinion that the world has a future reaching beyond the most distant frontiers of the imagination—and that is perhaps why, in spite of all his faults, so many scientists still count Francis Bacon their first and greatest spokesman: we may yet build a New Atlantis. The point is that when Thomas Burnet exhorted us to become "Adventurers for Another World," *he* meant the next world—but we mean this one.

Medical Research and the Individual

The patient, however humble and however ill, in whatever degree derelict and forlorn, has sacred rights which the physician must always put ahead of his burning curiosity.

W. B. BEAN

SCOPE

THE SUBJECT of this symposium, "Medicine and the Sanctity of Life," conjures up such a broad sweep of areas for consideration, one is confronted with the temptation to try to do too much, and having attempted all, achieve nothing. I have, therefore, sought for a theme which could be considered in depth, yet one which is relevant to medicine as a whole and certainly relevant to the sanctity of life. I believe I have found such a theme in the ethical problems arising in experimentation in man. I propose to limit my remarks to this subject. It is one which can run away with our passions, emotions, and judgment. It invites the grand and vague statement. It

114

HENRY K. BEECHER

is therefore necessary to define still further the precise limitations of the present discussion: *We are to be concerned here only with experimentation in one patient, not at all for his specific benefit, but, hopefully, for the benefit of patients in general.* A subdivision of this category is the hopelessly ill and suffering patient whose life is prolonged for "the sake of scientific studies." It is mentioned at all only to be condemned.

We are not at the moment to be concerned with the volunteer,[1] except as individual patients may volunteer for the

[1] Some have argued that there is no difference between normal subjects who volunteer and patients. There is. The volunteer usually does it for gain for himself: influence, prestige, good will of the experimenter, ego satisfaction or curiosity, the prisoner's reduction in penalties, money. The normal volunteer is usually a freer agent than the patient, who is part of a "captive group." The former can accept or refuse the opportunity; he knows for sure that he is to be a participant in an experiment. It is all too apparent in the following examples that

above purpose. We are not concerned with therapy for a specific patient. (The physician of course experiments constantly in treating the sick man, since no two patients are alike.)

Nothing in the remarks to follow should be construed as a general criticism of American medicine. It is excellent. It is sound. As with all other things human, it is not perfect in all of its aspects; certain practices in even the best institutions merit examination and re-examination from time to time.

One often hears it said these days that moral choices are always among shades of gray, never between black and white. This, of course, is not true. Choice sometimes *is* between black and white, and I suspect this is rather often the case. There is, for example, nothing grayish in the choice of whether one will or will not carry out health-endangering investigation in subjects without their knowledge or consent, as in the study involving hundreds of military men where known effective treatment for streptococcic throat infection was withheld and many cases of rheumatic fever ensued. Nor is there any difficulty in appraising the typhoid fever study, where effective treatment was withheld and more than a score of subjects died who, by the authors' own figures, would not have died if the effective treatment had not been withheld.

---

the patient, when not a true volunteer, often never had any such opportunity, sometimes never even knew he was the subject of experimentation. His well-being, his comfort, his health, and even his life can be jeopardized, even lost, without his understanding or prior consent. There are, certainly, differences between the two groups.

Nothing was said about consent; it is beyond reasonable doubt that valid consent was obtained.

The experienced clinician knows that if he has a good rapport with his patients they will often submit to inconvenience and even discomfort for the sake of "science." Excepting the extremely rare individual, they will not willingly risk their health or their life for a scientific experiment. It is wrong to assume otherwise. They will not do it. In the examples presented here, it is clear that the investigators have made the decision to risk the welfare of their subjects, not for their benefit, but for science in general, a decision that can be challenged on moral grounds. It will be widely charged that a serious disservice to medicine is effected by bringing these matters into the open for discussion. I am firmly convinced that to postpone discussion of them will, in the not distant future, do great damage to medicine, or I would not have taken the unpleasant and lonely road into this field.

It seems not to have occurred to these critics that medical progress founded on dishonesty, or exploitation of the doctor-patient relationship, or the injury or death of patients in such work—and all of these things have occurred repeatedly—does a greater harm to medicine than that charged. Indeed, *one* irresponsible experimenter can do very great harm to medicine as a whole. "Progress" in medicine founded on neglect of the patient's rights is on a downward course. It can only be heading for a disaster far wider than the welfare of medicine alone: It indicates a decay of appalling proportions in the moral values in our society.

117

James Reston, in speaking of present world attitudes, said, "If there has been a decline of decency in the modern world and a revolt against law and fair dealing, it is precisely because of the decline in the belief in each man as something precious." [2] It is unthinkable to accept progress in medicine founded on a patient defrauded of his rights. Such practice runs counter to all that medicine stands for.

PAST AND PRESENT

Several areas pertinent to the ethical aspects of experimentation in man lie near the heart of the matter: There is the fair question of whether, for all of our talk, we have truly and generally advanced in our informed care for the experimental patient's welfare. One supposes that the answer is, Yes, we have. But consider the following examples. If we knew of Queen Caroline's performance in 1754,[3] most of us would be shocked by it. Sir Hans Sloane describes, in 1756, how

The princess Anne, now princess royal of Orange, falling ill of the small-pox in such a dangerous way that I very much feared her life, the late queen Caroline, when princess of Wales, to secure her other children, and for the common good, begged the lives of six condemned criminals, who had not had the small-pox, in order to try this experiment of inoculation [upon] them. . . . To make a further tryal, the late queen Caroline procured half a dozen of the charity-children belonging to St. James's parish, who were inocu-

[2] *The New York Times* (April 18, 1965).
[3] H. K. Beecher, "Experimentation in Man," *Journal of the American Medical Association*, CLXIX (1959), 461–78.

118

lated, and all of them, except one (who had had the small-pox before, tho' she pretended not, for the sake of the reward) went thro' it with the symptoms of a favourable kind of that distemper.

This happened long ago, but I should like to refer to an example of the use of children two hundred years later, described in the New York *Herald-Tribune* of October 25, 1956.

Thirty-four infants, whose mothers are in the state reformatory for women here, have been fed live polio virus in their milk in a scientific experiment.

They were given the weakened virus to determine their antibody response while they still had temporary immunity acquired from their mothers. The work was in connection with a search for a live polio virus capable of being taken by mouth and producing long immunization with a single dose for each type of polio virus.

It appears to be true in this country, as it is in Britain [4] and probably in Denmark and Sweden, that clinical medicine in teaching hospitals has become dominated in the past twenty years by "investigators." However, I do not believe we are yet necessarily obliged to agree with Sir Heneage Ogilvie's extreme statement about England: "The science of experimental medicine is something new and sinister; for it is capable of destroying in our minds the old faith that we, the doctors, are the servants of the patients whom we have undertaken to care for, and, in the minds of the patients, the complete trust that they can place their own lives and the

[4] M. H. Pappworth, "Human Guinea Pigs: A Warning," *Twentieth Century*, CLXXI (Autumn, 1962), 66–75.

119

lives of their loved ones in our care." This warning emphasizes the importance of facing up to the ethical problems arising in the expansion of experimentation in man.

REASONS FOR URGENCY

Elsewhere I have listed a number of compelling reasons why further delay in coming to grips with the problems described here is unwise.[5] Briefly, they are these: Vast sums of money are now available for research in man. These will increase. (Consider the President's Commission on Heart Disease, Cancer and Stroke.) Every ambitious young physician knows he will not be appointed to a tenure post in a major medical school unless he has done creditable research. Thus, great pressures are exerted on the young man. Besides these "practical" points,[6] it must be recognized that there is a general awakening of social conscience. New remedies have a greater power for good or ill than was often the case in earlier times. New procedures are now often applied to communities, not just individuals, with multiplication of the hazards. The value of human experimentation has been widely recognized. Clinical research as a *profession* is a relatively new development (cf. clinical pharmacology).

Sir Heneage Ogilvie has commented harshly: "What is new in medicine is research by fraud." One could reply to

[5] H. K. Beecher, "Ethics and Clinical Research," *New England Journal of Medicine*, CCLXXIV (June 16, 1966), 1354–60.
[6] Robert Platt, *Doctor and Patient: Ethics, Morals, Government* (London and Tonbridge: Whitefriars Press, for Nuffield Provincial Hospitals Trust, 1963).

Ogilvie: What is old in medicine is fraudulent therapy, and this is what sound experimentation is designed to root out of the past and prevent in the future. Research in medicine is essential for progress, and ultimately studies must be made in man. The answer to the dilemma I have implied has, I believe, two chief parts. There is (a) *valid* consent. In fairness to the patient, for moral, sociological, and legal reasons this is a requirement not to be foregone, except (in my view) where there is no discernible risk and where discussion would likely vitiate the results sought, as in a comparison of morphine with a placebo. The difficulties in obtaining valid consent are often great and the results incomplete. These will be discussed in a moment. (b) A second and more dependable requirement than (a) is the presence of an informed, intelligent, skillful, compassionate, responsible investigator.

Some of the examples mentioned are clearly unethical owing to established lack of informed consent, and others owing to a clear failure of responsibility of the investigator. And in some cases both requirements are lacking.

VALID CONSENT

The central problem about which much in the field of experimentation in man revolves is that of valid consent. A quick reading of the Nuremberg Code and all other codes makes this sound like an easy and ordinary thing to obtain. It is not. The fallacies and difficulties in the application of the principle of consent deserve comment.

121

Most of the difficulties implied in the foregoing are solved if valid, meaningful consent can be obtained. If we do not have this, we may be in real difficulty.

NUREMBERG POINT NUMBER 1

This says: *The voluntary consent of the human subject is absolutely essential.*

This means that the person involved should have legal capacity to give consent; should be so situated as to be able to exercise free power of choice, without the intervention of any element of force, fraud, deceit, duress, over-reaching, or other ulterior form of constraint or coercion; and should have sufficient knowledge and comprehension of the elements of the subject matter involved as to enable him to make an understanding and enlightened decision. [Often impossible.] This latter element requires that before the acceptance of an affirmative decision by the experimental subject there should be made known to him the nature, duration, and purpose of the experiment; the method and means by which it is to be conducted; all inconveniences and hazards reasonably to be expected; and the effects upon his health or person which may possibly come from his participation in the experiments. [These are often unknown in the beginning.[7]]

The duty and responsibility for ascertaining the quality of the

[7] I have never understood why Claude Bernard's statement is so often quoted. He said in 1856, "Christian morals forbid only one thing, doing ill to one's neighbor. So among experiments that may be tried on man, those that can only do harm are forbidden, those that are harmless are permissible, and those that do good are obligatory" (quoted in C. J. Wiggers, "Human Experimentation, as Exemplified by the Career of Dr. William Beaumont," *Alumni Bulletin of Western Reserve University* [1950], pp. 60–65). The problem is, in the beginning one can hardly make such distinctions.

consent rests upon each individual who initiates, directs or engages in the experiment. It is a personal duty and responsibility which may not be delegated to another with impunity.[8]

Any questions I raise about point number 1 should by no means be construed as attacking the principle. Its application is absolutely essential, when this is possible, but there are times when it is not possible. Alfred North Whitehead once advised his reader to beware the fallacy of the misplaced concreteness. Anyone who believes that meaningful consent is often easily achieved is guilty of fallacious thinking.

"FULL KNOWLEDGE OF RISK"
AS A COMPONENT OF VALID CONSENT

How is the investigator to obtain valid consent when the risk involved in his proposed procedure is not known to himself or to anyone else?

Some commentators have taken the rigid view that no one can soundly consent to a risky enigma. In the case of a wholly new procedure, the risk cannot usually be known. In the case of a procedure that is well tried but new for the individual subject, the risk is of course less than in the preceding example but still not entirely clear. When drugs are administered, there is always the possibility in the individual case of drug sensitivity or idiosyncracy of serious degree.

There may be some risk in the simplest experimentation

[8] "The Medical Case," *Nuremberg Military Tribunals, Trials of War Criminals* (Washington, D.C.: U.S. Government Printing Office, 1947), II, 181–84.

in man. (I believe it was R. A. McCance who pointed out that the baby could suffer fatal injury if dropped while being weighed.) Since the risk is usually not known in the early stages of even simple procedures, one cannot require that full knowledge be an essential part of valid consent. To do so would block nearly all progress in experimentation. (And with this statement we seem to have slipped into the ends-justify-means argument, but this will be described below.)

Considerable or even great risk is not necessarily an absolute injunction against acceptance by the investigator or the subject. Indeed, some procedures have been associated with a fatal outcome and yet may still provide advantages great enough to outweigh the hazard involved. One cannot forbid what may be a perilous procedure on the basis of unknown risk alone. It seems to me, however, that great risk should usually be accepted only if the subject promises to profit directly from it. As pragmatists, we are obliged to agree that cardiac catheterization, whose risk was unknown in the beginning and which is now known to be fatal in some cases, is of such benefit to mankind that its continued use is mandatory. It has received the accolade of three Nobel Prizes. One distinguished investigator who often uses the technique of cardiac catheterization has said that he would never have considered it ethical to employ this in its early period, but now that it is of established value he considers its use permissible. This *post hoc* justification of risk assumed by others is questionable. Here is an example of initial consent that some would not have considered to be wholly valid, and yet the results achieved are everywhere accepted today. These are difficult, puzzling problems.

Some few individuals could doubtless be found who would say that "I am willing to risk my life and die if the experiment goes wrong." This is an easy rationalization of the puzzle just mentioned, difficult of achievement. In trying to face up to these issues we must recognize that this point of view can get us into deep water philosophically. We can grant that martyrdom for a sufficient cause has for many centuries been considered the noblest human act. The important phrase here is *sufficient cause*. The determination of this can be difficult to the point of impossible. Yet many agree that benefits found *post hoc* (cf. cardiac catheterization) sometimes seem *post hoc* to justify unknown risks.

Risk is, at times, necessary for progress. One hopes that advancement will be achieved. But one knows that even if it is not, the gallant human spirit will grow only if stimulated by selfless and promising adventures. In this sense the means have value while the ends may or may not. This situation is not, then, simply a case of ends justify means.

Pius XII had some trenchant comments on this:

In the first place it must be assumed that, as a private person, the doctor can take no measure or try no course of action without the consent of the patient. The doctor has no other rights or power over the patient than those which the latter gives him, explicitly or implicitly and tacitly. On his side, the patient cannot confer rights he does not possess. In this discussion the decisive point is the moral licitnessof the right a patient has to dispose of himself. Here is the moral limit to the doctor's action taken with the consent of the patient.

As for the patient, he is not absolute master of himself, of his body, or of his soul. He cannot, therefore, freely dispose of himself as he pleases. Even the reason for which he acts is of itself neither sufficient nor determining. The patient is bound to the imminent teleology laid down by nature. He has the right of *use*, limited by natural finality, of the faculties and powers of his human nature. Because he is a user and not a proprietor, he does not have unlimited power to destroy or mutilate his body and its functions.

The patient, then, has no right to involve his physical or psychic integrity in medical experiments or research when they entail serious destruction, mutilation, wounds or perils.

Sometimes it happens that a method cannot be used without injuring the rights of others or without violating some moral rule of absolute value. In such a case, although one rightly envisages and pursues the increase of knowledge, morally the method is not admissible. Why not? Because science is not the highest value, that to which all other orders of values—or in the same order of value, all particular values—should be subordinated. Science itself, therefore, as well as its research and acquisitions, must be inserted in the order of values. Here there are well defined limits which even medical science cannot transgress without violating higher moral rules.[9]

Difficulties in Communicating Risk

When the risk is known for the average, we are still up against uncertainty when we apply a given procedure to a

[9] Pope Pius XII, "The Moral Limits of Medical Research and Treatment" (address to the First International Congress on Histopathology of the Nervous System, Sept. 14, 1952).

given individual. In such cases there are always elements of uncertainty. The investigator may not know enough himself or he may not be an adequate expositor of risk. It is, of course, impossible to communicate risk to an incompetent: (1) infants and children, (2) the confused or mentally deficient, or (3) laymen who do not have the background of learning or intelligence to enable them to comprehend a complex technical proposal. (One can fairly raise the question as to whether those responsible for children or the mentally deficient have the right to consent to something they themselves will not experience.) As Seymour Kety once phrased it, "the investigator has no right to choose martyrs for science." [10]

The "Engineering" of Consent

I have quoted Edmond Cahn before, and I make no apology for doing it again. He said:

Of course, in the civilized societies of our day one does not resort to Nazi violence; one requests the subject of the proposed experiment to give his free consent. But can we rightly assume that when the consent is given, it is always morally acceptable?

One of the major malpractices of our era consists in the "engineering of consent." Sometimes this is effected simply by exploiting the condition of necessitous men, as in certain Indian states where thousands of consents to sexual sterilization have been purchased by offering a trivial bounty to the members of a destitute caste. Then again, consent may be "engineered" by the kind of psychologist who takes it for granted that his assistants and students

[10] S. S. Kety, personal communications, Nov. 6, 1967, and Feb. 26, 1958.

will submit to experiments and implies a threat to advancement if they raise objections. Or the total community may "engineer" a consent, as when the president, the generals, and the newspapers call with loud fanfare for a heroic crew of astronautical volunteers to attempt some ultrahazardous exploit.

It is worth considering that the destitute Indians who accept payment for sterilization can at least know what they are consenting to; the psychological and astronautical subjects cannot. Moreover, though the astronauts are fairly certain of winning some species of glory, the lady who submits to hypnosis in the interest of science is certain of scarcely anything. . . . Even a free consent must have moral limits in a society that honors human dignity, and honoring it, puts a ceiling-price on truth.[11]

THE CONSCIENCE AND RESPONSIBILITY OF THE INVESTIGATOR

Informed consent is important, and it must always be sought; but its weaknesses are great, as I have indicated in the above discussion: It is a goal toward which we strive and which we rarely attain in any complete sense. As pointed out by the British Medical Research Council (1953): To obtain the consent of the patient to a proposed investigation is not in itself enough.

Owing to the special relationship of trust that exists between a patient and his doctor, most patients will consent to any proposal that is made. Further, the considerations involved in a novel procedure are nearly always so technical as to prevent their being adequately understood by one who is not himself an expert. It must, therefore, be frankly recognized that, for practical purposes,

[11] E. Cahn, "The Lawyer as Scientist and Scoundrel: Reflection on Francis Bacon's Quadricentennial," *New York University Law Review*, XXXVI (1961), 1–12.

an inescapable moral responsibility rests with the doctor concerned for determining what investigations are, or are not, proposed to a particular patient or volunteer.

Nearly always his judgment will be accepted by the patient as decisive.

As mentioned earlier, it is apparent that the most dependable safeguard of the patient subjected to experimentation must be the conscience of the intelligent, informed, responsible, compassionate investigator. The reader can judge for himself whether the investigators in a given study have lived up to an acceptable ethical standard, bearing in mind that only the exceedingly rare subject will willingly jeopardize his health or his life. Where this is in fact the case and where more than a few subjects are involved, it will be evident that an unethical situation obtains. "Fox would go further and say that when in pursuance of research some part of normal treatment is to be withheld or some unestablished method applied or fresh symptoms caused or adventitious danger incurred, consent for an experiment ought to include the approval of a doctor acting on the patient's behalf." [12]

"STATISTICAL MORALITY"

At the Dartmouth conference on "The Great Issues of Conscience in Modern Medicine," Warren Weaver described statistical morality as derived from "the prejudice against even permitting any one known specific individual to sacrifice

[12] Platt, *Doctor and Patient*, p. 63; cf. O. E. Guttentag, "The Problem of Experimentation on Human Beings. II: The Physician's Point of View," *Science*, CXVII (1953), 207–10.

his life for the common good," and yet "we have to, in a great many circumstances, submit a lot of individuals to a partial risk" with the result that even though "the risk is only one in a million, when a million are involved, one man will be dead with our acquiescence." "It is a comfort to our conscience that we don't know *where* it occurred or *when* it occurred. But that individual is just as dead as though we knew all about it." [13] In such deep waters we strive for balance, but sometimes emerge with little more than questions and tangled arguments.

For example, in discussing new and uncertain risk against probable benefit, Lord Adrian spoke of the rise of mass radiography of the chest in Britain. Four-and-a-half million examinations were made in 1957. It has been calculated that bone marrow effects of the radiation might possibly have added as many as twenty cases of leukemia in that year; yet the examinations revealed eighteen thousand cases of pulmonary tuberculosis needing supervision, as well as thousands of other abnormalities. The twenty deaths from leukemia were only a remote possibility, but, Lord Adrian asks, if they were a certainty would they have been too high a price to pay for the early detection of tuberculosis in eighteen thousand people? [14]

[13] W. Weaver, "The Great Issues of Conscience in Modern Medicine" (address to the Dartmouth Conference, Hanover, N.H., Sept. 8–10, 1960).

[14] E. D. Adrian, "Priorities in Medical Responsibility" (Jephcott Lecture), *Proceedings of the Royal Society of Medicine*, LVI (1963), 523–28.

ENDS, MEANS

"This is the scientist's moral: that there is no distinction between ends and means." [15] At the end of his short life the mathematician and philosopher, W. K. Clifford, had this to say nearly a hundred years ago; its essence is the same as Bronowski's.

If I steal money from any person, there may be no harm done by the mere transfer of possession; he may not feel the loss, or it may even prevent him from using the money badly. But I cannot help doing this great wrong towards Man, that I make myself dishonest. What hurts society is not that it should lose its property, but that it should become a den of thieves; for then it must cease to be society. This is why we ought not to do evil that good may come; for at any rate this great evil has come, that we have done evil and are made wicked thereby.[16]

It is curious to see how often intelligent and considerate men fall into the fallacy that ends justify means. This tendency is common in attempts to justify unethical experimentation. An experiment does not become ethical *post hoc;* it is ethical at its inception, or it is not.

The usual procedure of justification is to say that the progress of science "required" the experimentation done in the uninformed, unconsenting patient. Or it is said by some medical editors that objection to certain unethical studies "would block progress." These typical remarks have been

[15] J. Bronowski, *Science and Human Values* (New York: Harper and Row, 1965).
[16] Quoted in *ibid.*, p. 65.

voiced many times; so often, in fact, that one wonders where we in the medical schools have failed. Sometimes such remarks are made by men who could not care less about ethical failure. Far more often they are made by young and old who have simply failed to see clearly the issues involved, owing to failure to consider these matters.

It is often said that we live in a materialistic age, in a materialistic world. A considerable number of individuals are in the unhappy and untenable position of accepting the results of unethical experimentation while disapproving the means. This is "the scientist's ethic, and the poet's, and every creator's: that the end for which we work exists and is judged only by the means which we use to reach it" (Bronowski, 1965).

The acceptance of risk per se is not necessarily unethical, and to say that there is need for balancing risk with commensurate gain is to state a principle which if properly applied does not violate the other principle that ends do not justify means. Such a balancing of interests has for many years been a respectable theory of American law. But as W. J. Curran has emphasized, the exponents of "the natural law" or "fundamental justice" assert that no end of social justification warrants depriving an individual of certain basic rights.[17]

[17] W. J. Curran, "Legal Codes in Scientific Research Involving Human Subjects" (address to the Conference on Law and Science, International Academy of Law and Science, London, July 20, 1965).

THE LAW AND HUMAN EXPERIMENTATION

More than three hundred years ago Hugo Grotius "found in the natural law the means of preserving society. Under this system, laws are tested on the basis of 'right reasons' as being in conformity or in conflict with the 'rational and social nature of man.' In other words, *man* is the central value: the society exists to serve man. Man has certain basic rights which cannot be taken from him by the state." [18] Violations of this concept are evident in the material presented here.

As Curran points out further, throughout the Western world there is growing legal theory which recognizes the value of man. Thus Article 7 of the Draft Covenant on Civil and Political Rights of the United Nations says, in part, "No one shall be subjected without his free consent to medical or scientific experimentation." (The difficulties inherent in this have already been discussed.)

There is little use of speaking forcefully, as some have done, on the use of present laws to protect human experimentation. One must ask, What laws, what legal structure? One can say only that the individual has certain basic rights protected by law. However valuable for the human race a new procedure appears to be, if disaster occurs, the high-minded purpose of the investigator will give him no legal protection. The *Duke Law Journal* attempts to take a more cheerful view of the matter, however; the legal implications of psychological research with human subjects have been

[18] *Ibid.*

given a puzzled consideration in that journal, which states firmly, but surprisingly, "If a legal action is brought against the scientific experimenter, its result will depend upon the existence of a privilege conferred on the experimenter by society, determined by balancing the risk of possible harm to the subject against the potential returns to society. . . ." [19] Here is the untenable view that ends justify means.

This approach is echoed by the Chief, Stress and Fatigue Section, Aero Medical Laboratory, Wright-Patterson Air Force Base, Captain George E. Ruff, who says,

We feel that the limited possibilities of danger in our work are more than outweighed by its potential returns. Both the need for data on personality structure and function and on environments important in space flight are more than enough to justify these particular experiments. Such reasons would probably not justify studies where a high percentage of the subjects might be harmed. [20]

Legal matters in the area of psychological experimentation are at least as indefinite as they are in other areas. One hopes that today Captain Ruff's remarks would not have received higher official approval.

The only thing the law has said about medical experimentation as such is that a man "experiments to his peril." When experimentation in man has led to legal processes, the only legal code I am familiar with [21] tests the question as to

[19] "Legal Implications of Psychological Research with Human Subjects" (Comments), *Duke Law Journal* (1960), pp. 265–74.

[20] G. E. Ruff, Letter to the *Duke Law Journal*, May 27, 1959, *Duke Law Journal* (1960), p. 267.

[21] Beecher, "Experimentation in Man."

whether the studies involved were in accord with the accepted standards of practice of the medical community. Research, if new and valuable, can hardly be in such accord. If it is truly useful, it goes beyond standard practices. It is new. It is different. It is unlike the old.

Parents and guardians can, of course, legally give permission for procedures designed to benefit their charges, whether children or the mentally incompetent. It is generally considered to be also within their right to give permission for ethical procedures not for the subjects' benefit. But in a strict interpretation of English law, and if any risk is involved, this is illegal. The issue is not quite so clear in American law: The Supreme Judicial Court of Massachusetts ruled that children at the age of understanding might give organs for transplantation, but there is the Bonner *vs.* Moran case (1941) where a fifteen-year-old boy donated skin to his cousin who had suffered severe burns. This was done at the behest of an aunt, without the knowledge of the mother, who was ill and knew nothing of the plan. The court's view was that if the mother had consented, this would have been satisfactory. Some hold, however, that morally no one has the right to subject others under his authority to procedures involving risk which he himself is not to undergo.

With the recent well-known activities of the Federal Food and Drug Administration, it has been stated again and again in certain types of investigation, where consent would vitiate sound experimental design (especially where the "double unknowns" approach is mandatory, as it usually is with subjective responses) and provided that no discernible risk is involved, that consent might be foregone. (Some have argued that the use of placebos in such a study is unethical. But it has been found by many investigators that placebos are indeed powerful tools in the alleviation of pain, for example, with more than half as much effectiveness as the standard dose of morphine; it is evident that a placebo is not "nothing" when used in a subjective symptom area, at least.[22] It is a useful analgesic tool, not so effective as the standard morphine but still useful.) But now comes the statement of Dr. Frances O. Kelsey, who says that the legislative intent, where consent can be foregone, was only to cover emergencies when consent could not be obtained in time. She says, "There is no basis for concluding that such exceptions would include circumstances in which the investigator feels that informed consent would interfere with the design of the experiment or would disturb the 'doctor-patient' relationship."[23] I had written repeatedly to the then Commissioner George P. Larrick to ask him just what the basis is for this "ruling" by Dr. Kelsey. After many months he essentially affirmed Dr. Kelsey's statement.

If Dr. Kelsey's "ruling" is to be universally applied, it could have some harsh consequences; for example, a patient with a possibly fatal illness might be awakened to the situa-

[22] H. K. Beecher, *Measurement of Subjective Responses: Quantitative Effects of Drugs* (New York: Oxford University Press, 1959).

[23] F. O. Kelsey, Hearings Before the Subcommittee on Reorganization and International Organization, U.S. Senate Committee on Government Operations, 88th Cong., Washington, D.C., 1964), p. 2454.

tion by the "tell-all" approach when a controlled clinical trial was necessary for evaluation of the disease or a suggested remedy. In other circumstances, the use of placebos may be required to estimate how much of a subjective component is present in a given drug effect. Discussion of the controls with the subject could destroy possibility of success.

QUESTIONABLE OR UNACCEPTABLE SUBJECTS FOR EXPERIMENTATION
Patients Soon to Die

In my view, experimentation, even with consent, is not advisable in some cases. Others may disagree, but I firmly believe that those who are about to die, or who are in danger of sudden death, are in most cases not acceptable as volunteer subjects for experimentation, even if they are clear mentally and their judgment is unquestionably sound. I believe this for the rather obvious reason that death may occur during the experimental period for reasons which may have no relationship to the study. The death casts an unmerited cloud over the investigator and his project, however innocent he may have been and however potentially valuable his project may be.

Captive Groups

I do not believe that captive groups *in general* present a good source of "volunteers." The reason is plain: Where possibilities for coercion exist, however subtle they may be, the use of members of such a group may violate the requirements for valid consent. Such volunteers must be suspect whether

137

they are one's laboratory personnel, military personnel, medical students, civil or military prisoners, or one's ward patients. Prisoners of war are never acceptable subjects. This can be stated categorically.

The use of medical students as subjects for research has been accepted for a long time, but no instructor should permit *his* students to be used in his investigations. One cannot deny the great benefits to accrue from the use of civil prisoners, especially in wartime studies. The prospect of an award to the subject, in terms of reduction of time of imprisonment or parole or pardon, may really function as an almost overwhelming bribe which seems to violate the necessary requirements of the principle of consent. Once again we are up against choices among shades of gray. The exigencies of national peril, the *bonum communum* may excuse the careful use of such subjects. The ice is thin. In weighing the pros and cons of such use, one had better face the fact that this was precisely the rationalization claimed by the Nazis.

A Dozen Published Examples of Unethical or Questionably Ethical Papers

The following dozen examples are chosen from a random sample of fifty.[24] They illustrate various kinds of experimentation of concern in this study. Specific references are not given here, although they are available to the editor, for I have no wish to point to individuals but rather to practices

[24] Beecher, "Ethics and Clinical Research."

found in industry, in the universities, and university hospitals and private hospitals, in the government, the army, the air force, the navy, the Public Health Service, the National Institutes of Health, and the Veterans Administration. Indeed, examples can be found wherever experimentation in man occurs to any significant extent.

A word should be added here concerning frequency. The original seventeen examples were easily tripled to fifty. These 50 contained 186 further references to similar work. One of the finest journals specializing in human experimentation was studied in 1964; one hundred consecutive human investigations showed twelve to be questionably ethical. Thus, it is evident that the problems dealt with here are by no means rare.

Example 1. Eighteen children, three and one-half months to eighteen years of age, were selected from those about to undergo surgery for congenital heart disease. In the course of this, eleven were to have total thymectomy and seven were to serve as controls. Total thymectomy is not usually part of the primary cardiovascular surgery involved, and while it may not add greatly to the hazards of the necessary surgery, the authors are aware—and make it clear—that the eventual effects of thymectomy carried out in children are not known. This work is proposed as part of a long-range study of "the growth and development of these children over the years." As a part of this experimentation, full-thickness skin homografts were secured from an unrelated adult donor and sutured to the chest wall of the children—no part of the necessary surgery. No difference in the skin-homograft survival was observed in the two groups.

Example 2. In this study of cyclopropane, twenty-nine of the thirty-one patients studied were Negro. Average duration of the study was three hours (two to four-and-a-half hours). "Minor surgical procedures" were carried out in all but one subject. Moderate to deep anesthesia with endotracheal intubation and controlled respiration were used (not usual or necessary for minor surgery). Carbon dioxide was injected into the closed respiratory system until cardiac arrhythmias appeared. Toxic levels of carbon dioxide were achieved and maintained for considerable periods. In the control period four subjects exhibited ventricular extrasystoles. During cyclopropane anesthesia a variety of pathological cardiac arrhythmias occurred. When the carbon dioxide tension was elevated above normal, ventricular extrasystoles were more numerous than when the carbon dioxide tension was normal. "Ventricular arrhythmias were continuous in one subject for ninety minutes. . . ." It is well-known that such arrhythmias may lead to fatal fibrillation of the heart.

Example 3. In order to study the sequence of ventricular contraction in human bundle branch block, simultaneous catheterization of both ventricles was carried out in twenty-two subjects; right heart catheterization was carried out in the usual manner; the left heart was catheterized transbronchially. Extrasystoles were produced by tapping the epicardium in subjects with normal myocardium while they were undergoing thoracotomy. Simultaneous pressures were

140

measured in both ventricles through needle puncture in this group.

Example 4. This study was directed to determining the period of infectivity of infectious hepatitis. Artificial induction of hepatitis was carried out in a state institution for mentally defective children (many five to eight years old).

The authors give references to two earlier papers where their "justification" is presented. It is repeated here and is as follows:

It was inevitable that most of the newly admitted susceptible mentally retarded children would acquire the infection . . . [the disease] was especially mild at . . . facilities were available to provide optimum medical and nursing care . . . and [*post hoc*] observations on more than fifty patients who acquired artificially induced hepatitis at . . . reveal that the average experimental disease observed was even milder than the observed natural infection.

The parents gave consent for the intramuscular injection or oral administration of the virus.

Granted that the parents "consented," nothing is said as to what was told them concerning the appreciable hazards involved. This study does not become ethical because the experimental infections produced a mild form of the disease. A death rate of one or two cases per one thousand is not negligible. There is no assurance that the sequelae in the years to come will be innocuous.

The argument that the children would get the infection anyhow is not valid. If epidemic conditions were continuing, admissions should have been suspended and quarantine imposed as in any other epidemic.

A resolution adopted by the World Medical Association states explicitly: "Under no circumstances is a doctor permitted to do anything which would weaken the physical or mental resistance of a human being except from strictly therapeutic or prophylactic indications imposed in the interest of the patient." There is no right to risk an injury to one individual for the benefit of others.

Example 5. Live cancer cells were injected into twenty-two human subjects as part of a study of immunity to cancer. According to a recent review, the subjects (hospitalized patients) were "merely told they would be receiving 'some cells.' " ". . . the word cancer was entirely omitted. . . ." According to the review, the question was raised as to whether the investigators would use themselves as subjects. The review contained the following quotation, "I would not have hesitated," the principal investigator said, "if it would have served a useful purpose. . . . I do not regard myself as indispensable—if I were not doing this work someone else would be . . . and I did not regard the experiment as dangerous. But let's face it, there are relatively few skilled cancer researchers, and it seemed stupid to take even the little risk."

Example 6. Cancer investigators who have chosen not to subject themselves to cancer implantation, because there was some risk, may thus have avoided personal disasters. This is emphasized by a recent case. Melanoma was transplanted from a daughter to her volunteering and informed mother.

The authors say they did this "in the hope of gaining a little better understanding of cancer immunity and in the hope that the production of tumor antibodies might be helpful in the treatment of the cancer patient." Inasmuch as the daughter died the day following the transplant of the tumor into her mother, the latter hope seems to have been more theoretical than practical. (While her demise may have been somewhat unexpected at the time it occurred, the daughter's condition was described as "terminal" at the time the mother volunteered to be a recipient.) The primary implant was widely excised the twenty-fourth day after it had been placed in the mother. She died from metastatic melanoma on the 451st day after transplantation. The authors say, "We feel that the evidence is conclusive that this patient died of diffuse melanoma which metastasized from a small piece of transplanted tumor."

Example 7. This is a study of the effect of exercise on cardiac output and pulmonary artery pressure in (a) normal persons (eight patients whose diseases were not related to the cardiovascular system), (b) those with cardiovascular disease (eight with congestive failure severe enough to require recently complete bed rest and six with hypertension; two with aortic insufficiency; seven with mitral stenosis), and (c) pulmonary emphysema (five patients).

Cardiac catheterization was carried out and the catheter then inserted into the right or left main branch of the pulmonary artery. The brachial artery was usually catheterized; sometimes the radial or femoral arteries were catheterized. The subjects exercised in a supine position by pushing their feet against weighted pedals. "The ability of these patients to carry on sustained work was severely limited by weakness and dyspnea." Several were in severe failure.

Example 8. TriA (triacetyloleandomycin) was introduced for the treatment of infection with gram positive organisms. Spotty evidence of hepatic dysfunction emerged, especially in children, and so the present study was undertaken in "50 patients [. . . which] included mental defectives or juvenile delinquents" who were inmates of a children's center. No disease other than acne was present; the drug was given for treatment of this. The ages of the subjects ranged from thirteen to thirty-nine years. "By the time half the patients had received the drug for four weeks, the high incidence of significant hepatic dysfunction . . . led to the discontinuation of administration to the remainder of the group at three weeks." (However, only two weeks after the start of the administration of the drug, 54 per cent of the patients showed abnormal excretion of bromsulfalein.) Eight patients with marked hepatic dysfunction were transferred to the hospital "for more intensive study." Liver biopsy was carried out in these eight patients and repeated in four of them. Liver damage was evident. Four of these hospitalized patients, after their liver function tests returned to normal, received a "challenge" dose of the drug. Within two days hepatic dysfunction was evident in three of the four patients. In one patient a second challenge dose was given after the first challenge and again led to evidence of abnormal liver function. Flocculation tests remained abnormal in some patients as long as five weeks after discontinuance of the drug.

An editorial in a British journal comments on this study: ". . . juvenile delinquency in the United States obviously carries hazards which many of us had not previously suspected. The pimpled gangster of today may find himself the bilious guinea pig of tomorrow. It seems a little hard, perhaps, for a boy who has spent his formative years learning how to dodge flick-knives to fall victim to intercostal perforation by the Menghini needle."

Example 9. Forty-five patients in shock were given l-norepinephrine during light cyclopropane anesthesia. An anesthetic was required for surgical reasons. It is to be recalled that the combination of epinephrine and cyclopropane is usually considered very dangerous; l-norepinephrine has a structure similar to that of epinephrine. Animal work referred to suggests that the combination of l-norepinephrine and cyclopropane is dangerous. These authors, because of a liking for cyclopropane, decided to try the latter combination notwithstanding evidence against it, and also despite the fact that nineteen of the forty-five patients had preoperative clinical and electrocardiographic evidence of moderate-to-severe myocardial disease. They conclude that, "The simultaneous administration of light cyclopropane anesthesia and a continuous intravenous infusion of dilute levoarterenol [l-norepinephrine] does not appear to be as dangerous as hitherto believed."

145

Example 10. "Rheumatic fever can be prevented by adequate treatment of the preceding streptococcal respiratory infection," so say the authors of this article, based on studies carried out six years and four years previously. They also say, "The physician can ensure adequate therapy for the prevention of rheumatic fever by the parenteral administration of penicillin." Notwithstanding this definite knowledge they withheld definitive treatment and gave placebos to 109 military men, while Benzathine Penicillin G was given to others, in 2 doses, for a total of 257 men.

The therapy each patient received was determined automatically by his military serial number arranged so that more men received penicillin than received placebo. "In the small group of patients studied 2 definite cases of acute rheumatic fever and 1 of acute nephritis developed in the control patients, whereas these complications did not occur among the [257] patients who received the DBED penicillin."

Example 11. The sulfonamides were for many years the only antibacterial drugs available for treatment of acute streptococcic pharyngitis. This therapy was effective in shortening the duration of the illness and in reducing the suppurative complications. The present investigators set out to determine if the serious nonsuppurative complications—rheumatic fever and acute glomerulonephritis—would be reduced by this treatment. This study was made despite the investigator's knowledge that "penicillin and other antibiotics will prevent the subsequent development of rheumatic fever."

The subjects were 261 hospital patients. A control group of

264 men also with exudative group A streptococcus was included. The latter group received only nonspecific therapy, no sulfadiazine. The total group denied the effective penicillin comprised 525 men.

Rheumatic fever was diagnosed in 14 of the 251 (5.4 per cent) of those treated with sulfadiazine. In the control group, 11 of the 264 (4.2 per cent) developed rheumatic fever. Thus, twenty-five men were crippled, perhaps for life.

A medical officer present has stated in writing that the subjects were not informed, did not consent, and were not even aware they were the subjects of an experiment, yet admittedly twenty-five got rheumatic fever. According to this same medical officer, *more than seventy* men from whom known definitive treatment was withheld were on the wards with rheumatic fever when he was there.

Example 12. When a diseased patient comes to the physician for treatment, this connotes consent for therapy. Ethical problems can still be present. For example, chloramphenicol has long been recognized as an effective treatment for typhoid fever. To withhold this effective remedy can be a life-or-death decision. In the present example, 408 charity patients are considered: 251 were treated with chloramphenicol and of these 20 died (death rate, 7.97 per cent). Symptomatic treatment was given but chloramphenicol withheld in 157, and of these 36 died (death rate of 22.93 per cent). This was done in order to determine the relapse rate under the two conditions of therapy. In other words, according to the data presented, twenty-three additional patients died in the course of this study, patients who would not have been expected to do so if they had not been denied established therapy. These investigators having previously indicated the efficacy of chloramphenicol in the treatment of typhoid fever, evidently believed that *they* had the right to choose these martyrs for science, twenty-three of them.

Death Rates

Experts have estimated that catheterization of the right heart causes about one death per one thousand cases; left heart, five per one thousand cases (cf. examples 3 and 7). The death rate from percutaneous liver biopsy is estimated at one to three per one thousand cases (cf. example 8); anesthesia deaths at one per two thousand cases (cf. examples 2 and 9).

EDITORIAL RESPONSIBILITY

The British Medical Research Council clearly states its view of editorial responsibility (1953):

It cannot be assumed that it will be evident to every reader that the investigations being described were unobjectionable. Unless such is made unmistakably clear misconceptions can arise. In this connection a special responsibility devolves upon the editors, and editorial boards, of scientific journals . . . it is desirable that editors and editorial boards, before accepting any communication, should not only satisfy themselves that the appropriate requirements have been fulfilled, but may properly insist that the reader is left in no doubt that such is indeed the case.

In a 1960 study of sixty-one American medical journals carried out by Irving Ladimer, then of the Law-Medicine Research Institute of Boston University, and under the direction of William Curran, the question was asked, "Do you [editors] believe that concern for the social obligations of clinical research activity is a proper part of editorial responsibility?" The answers ranged from strong "yes, of course," replies, 58 per cent (thirty-five), to equally strong "no" replies, 28 per cent (seventeen). In the latter group it was said that "the ethical responsibility for clinical research must remain with the researcher and his sponsors, who, they felt, were adequately aware of their social obligations." This seems unrealistic in view of the examples cited above. As one editor put it, "the implications of effectively monitoring the standards of conducting experiments either with humans or animals would be highly antagonistic to the perpetration and expansion of the research process." [25] This contrasts with Pius XII's question and affirmation: "Why not? Because science is not the highest value to which all other orders of values . . . should be subordinated."

In this same study 85 per cent (forty-five) of the editors replied that they had no policy, formal or informal, for evaluating the degree of social responsibility in the articles under consideration. The policy of the British Medical Research Council seems to be sounder.

The fact that the editors and editorial boards of prominent journals would have recently accepted the questionable ma-

[25] I. Ladimes, "Survey of Professional Journals: Editorial Responsibility in Clinical Research" (unpublished data from a symposium directed by W. A. Curran, Boston University Law–Medicine Research Institute, 1960).

terial presented here is a prime indication of the extent of the problem and the need for a re-examination of editorial policy where experimentation in man is concerned.

A difficult and serious problem arises when an editor is confronted with truly valuable data unethically obtained. Such have often been accepted and published without comment. It has been suggested that publication might be accompanied by stern editorial comment. (It would be most difficult to do this and avoid a suggestion of hypocrisy.) A sounder handling would be to deny publication, and thereby deter other irresponsible investigators. It can be argued that the real loss of the specific material in question would be far less than the moral loss to medicine if such unethically obtained data were published.

In the recent Mapp Decision by the United States Supreme Court,[26] we can see a parallel: Evidence obtained illegally is not to be used in state or federal courts, however valuable to the ends of justice such evidence may be.

IN CONCLUSION

In this country, as well as in others, medical schools are dominated by investigators. In the last two or three decades, few if any individuals in the leading schools have achieved professorships until they have proved themselves productive in research. In too many instances this has led to the obsession that *all* must do research; "publish or perish" is not only a tired cliché, it is often a guiding principle. It seems probable

[26] Mapp *vs.* Ohio, 376 U.S. 643 (1961).

that this milieu is responsible, partly at least, for the scramble to make new observations in man, a milieu where the individual's rights are sometimes ruthlessly ignored. There is a prevalence of examples to illustrate this.

It may be trite to say it, but firm application of the golden rule would obviate many of the difficulties in the field of experimentation in man. Ideally this is to be coupled with adherence to the principle of *informed* consent where the hazards are reasonably well-known; and where the hazards are not known, this too is to be made clear. It is also, more importantly, to be coupled with the presence of a truly responsible investigator. Finally, it seems evident that editors and editorial boards have a profound responsibility to refuse to publish papers based upon unethical or questionably ethical procedures. Until these things are accepted, it is possible that ethical problems arising in human experimentation will increase in volume as well as in kind. It is a curious thing that the rights of the individual, so much discussed today, are so often ignored in human experimentation.

Moral rules alter with human development. As our insight into the problems illustrated here increases, we can approach them with increasing honesty and compassion and consideration for the rights of others and thus contribute to the sanctity of life.

Social Ethics and the Sanctity of Life: A Summary

I suppose it is inevitable—because of my place on this program if not because of the discipline I represent—that I am expected to deliver the benediction, though there are others here who could perform that function more appropriately (and perhaps they have already done so). At any rate, I would like to say that I am in a mood very different from that of wanting to bestow blessings. Indeed, I would like publicly to confirm Dr. Medawar's surmise that there are wicked philosophers; and I think I know why. It is because of the frustration they experience as a result of the role they are so often called upon to play: they are asked to summarize life, and in the course of their preparation of the summary, life passes them by.

Bertrand Russell once characterized the real task of philosophy as being twofold: first, to make complicated things simple, and second, to make simple things complicated. I

ABRAHAM KAPLAN

have taken these as my aims in this summary—to supplement what has already been said, not only by simplifying what was complicated, but also by complicating what appear to me to have been oversimplifications. In pursuit of these aims, and especially the second, it will be necessary to address myself not only to what has been said but also, and perhaps more significantly, to what has *not* been said. Alfred North Whitehead once advised that if we are interested in the philosophy of a particular society we must look, not at what was written in that society, but at what was left unwritten. It is in our tacit assumptions that we most clearly reveal our working philosophies.

One more prefatory remark—though perhaps it is more than prefatory, but rather a suggested formulation for the single theme, if there be one, of the whole symposium. Our task, as several members of the symposium have already made explicit, is not so much to offer solutions for the problems of the sanctity of life, but rather to raise these problems in an effective way. I might go further and say that they are problems for which no solutions exist, for which no solutions *can* exist. We can solve some problems in human life, but they are usually the less significant ones. Those that are more significant we do not solve, but at best we only *cope* with them. This is to say that we have no way of disposing of them; at best we learn to live with them, and go on to the next. I believe that this characterizes the problems with which the symposium has been concerned, as well as some related problems with which we were not concerned, though in my opinion we should have been. It is tempting to imagine that if we are clever enough, or well enough advised, we can dispose of these matters once for all. This is not possible; but hopefully, we can learn to live with the ever-present threats to the sanctity of life and still preserve some sense of self-respect and human decency.

What are the problems of medical ethics with which we have been occupied? It seems to me that we can identify them in a very simple way. They are those that we would be coping with if we lived in a society which somehow feels that life is at best only a necessary evil. First is the problem of contraception—how to prevent life from coming into existence at all. If we do not succeed in that, we face the problem of abortion—how to destroy it once it has begun. Next we move to the problem of "genetic engineering," as Shils called it—how to reshape it in our own image, for apparently it is not quite acceptable as it is. If we are not capable of modifying life, we have at any rate the problem of medical experimentation—how we can best learn what can be done with it. And if all else fails, we come finally to the problem of euthanasia—how we can put an end to life which we have been powerless to prevent or improve upon.

In sober vein we recognize, of course, that these formulations of the problems pervert our real concerns. Yet there is an irony in the fact—or what I suppose to be fact—that our deliberations on the sanctity of life take place against the background of a deep and widespread preoccupation with death that is characteristic of our culture. The sign on the platform to which reference has several times been made as reminiscent of the mortuary has done more than provide occasion for wit; it has, I think, put literally before us a familiarly morbid interest and attitude.[1] I do not mean anything as metaphysical or speculative as the Freudian death wish. I mean something that we can identify in easily observable patterns in our culture for facing and dealing with death.

In what has been called the American way of death, the high cost of dying is not surprising. For in much of our art and our religion, to say nothing of the mass media, death is associated with beauty, peace, loveliness—in short, with much of what is most precious in life. The magnificent cemeteries to which we transpose our Loved Ones seem designed

[1] The sign, which read "The Sanctity of Life," was printed in Gothic-style lettering and heavily edged in black.

to be saying to us, "Don't grieve for the dead—they never had it so good!" There is a story of a visitor to such a place who, overwhelmed by the beauty of the parkland, the marbles and bronzes, the music floating through the trees, murmured in admiration and envy, "Ah, that's living!"

I am saying that in our time there is a cult of death that provides the backdrop against which we must view the problems of the sanctity of life. Our technology seems never to reach greater heights than when it is put to the service of destruction. In that service it seems most ingenious, most efficient, even most sleekly beautiful. Norbert Wiener, one of the founders of our cybernetic technology, has called attention to the irony that our purposive machines, capable of attaining goals that they themselves set, owe much of their early development to the design of antiaircraft batteries that can follow and destroy a maneuvering target.

We have talked several times of the moral consensus on which we must rely in coping with the problems of the sanctity of life. But that consensus is significantly limited by another point of view in which it is death that is sanctified, not life. We know that outlook as characteristic of the regimes of Hitler, Stalin, and the Fascists; but as Erich Fromm and others have pointed out, it is also to be found in our own time and place. I am less distressed, for example, by what is called violence in the streets and the rising crime rate than I am by the fact that bystanders often do nothing, even when murder is being done before their very eyes. What is involved here is more than the dissociation from humanity in not keeping our brothers; it is the dissociation from life in prizing death. A threatened suicide, to take another example, often becomes only a public spectacle, and voices are heard egging him on to the final step. Our culture glosses over both the fact of death and the feelings evoked by confrontation with that ultimate fact.

I want now to put into perspective the problems of the sanctity of life that have been discussed in the symposium by calling attention to some that were not discussed—mentioned, perhaps, but with a brevity grossly disproportionate to their relative importance.

First, of course, is the problem of war—not merely the threat of war but its continuing actuality in modern society. Surely, however special our individual interests and backgrounds may be, we cannot begin to cope with the problems of the sanctity of life without dealing with that question.

Second—though not necessarily in importance—is the problem of starvation, and more generally, the problems of food, clothing, and shelter, and the related questions posed by the population explosion. These problems, too, are a widespread and continuing actuality.

A third problem—understandably troubling to one who comes from the environs of Detroit, but of real concern to all of us—is the problem of automobile safety. Dr. Medawar pointed out that the automobile is the principal single cause of death in the prime of manhood. I might add that more children die of accidents than of all infectious and parasitic diseases put together. And the rate of accidental death in the

United States is, I believe, the second highest in the world. Reference was made earlier to Warren Weaver's concept of the "statistical morality" that is involved in this situation. Because as a society we do not intend specific accidental deaths and have no knowledge of them in their specificity, we feel that no moral issue is involved; yet we adopt social patterns whose inexorable consequence is death to tens of thousands.

Any real concern for the sanctity of life in our culture must address itself to these problems—and to others, like suicide, of which we have hardly spoken at all—as well as to the special problems of medical ethics that have occupied the attention of this symposium.

Let me next pick up the thread of some thoughts put before us by Mr. Ramsey that seem to me to have important implications for the ways in which we must cope with the problems of the sanctity of life. I am referring to what he said about the idea of rational sacrifice and Paul Tillich's view of the ambiguity of all finite sacrifice.

The implication I would like to make explicit is this. We are caught up, all of us, in what I might call "the paradox of life." The paradox consists in this, that it is the melancholy fate of all the living that we must feed on life itself. We live, ultimately, only because others have died.

In other cultures, especially in Asia, the concept of the sanctity of life would be taken in so comprehensive a sense as to include the whole animal kingdom. Vegetarianism in its various grades becomes in this perspective a moral issue and not a question of health or nutrition. Schopenhauer remarks that when one animal feeds on another the pleasure of the eater is never so great as the pain of the one being eaten. We may dismiss the moral claims of vegetarianism—if we think of them at all—as sentimentality. But most of us, I think, would also acknowledge the degradation of our sense of the sanctity of life that would follow our visit to a slaughterhouse.

What is undeniably more than a matter of sentimentality is the burden of recognizing that it is not the death merely of other animals that makes our lives possible, but the death of other human beings. We are here only because others have moved aside to make way for us. Death must be conceptualized as a necessary part of life. This conception, as Mr. Ramsey pointed out, is an important component of the Judaeo-Christian teaching, but it is not easy to learn and to live with. For it seems to put us in a situation not of our own making, in which we are inescapably involved in the destruction of what we most cherish. It may be harder to accept sacrifice than to perform it.

There is a close parallel, and perhaps a metaphysical identity, between the paradox of life and the paradox of liberty that affects so much of our political life—that it is necessary to restrict certain of our liberties in order to maximize all of them. The traffic policeman, or his surrogate in the signal, tells me when and where I can move about the streets, and thereby is unquestionably denying me a free choice; yet, were it not for such a denial, it is possible that I would not be able to move freely through the streets at all. For the sake of peace

159

it may be necessary sometimes to fight. Our recognition of the sanctity of life may sometimes demand of us a course of action whose consequence is the taking of life.

Before turning to some further implications for our ways of coping with these problems, there is one more core problem of the symposium that I wish to speak of—the moral responsibility of science. I do not believe that this problem can be dismissed as lightly as Dr. Medawar pretended to dismiss it—though he went on at some length to explain why we need not occupy ourselves with it for very long.

Let me say first that *if* the problem is so posed as to force a choice between the "two cultures," I have no hesitation about where to take my stand—with science. (But I take it that none of us believes that there really is a choice to be made here.) In his *History of European Morals*, W. H. Lecky remarks that the inventor of anaesthesia contributed more to human happiness than all the moral philosophers from Socrates to John Stuart Mill—and beyond, I would add. No one who has ever suffered severe pain could fail to agree with this assessment, whatever his professional commitments.

Yet we cannot simply point to the good that science has done and, as for the evil, content ourselves with the observation that the possibilities of harm have always existed. Of course they have always existed, but new possibilities have now come into play. Possibilities for evil grow commensurately with the possibilities for good. The problem, to be sure, is an old one, and continuous in human history. There is an epigram of the pre-Socratic philosopher Heraclitus which puns on the word "bios," from which we get words like "biology," but which also designated the archer's bow: "Its name is life but its work is death." The name of science may be life—without the understanding, prediction, and control of nature that science has provided, modern life would not be possible; but it is also undeniable that apparently a large part of the work of science is the work of death. Science has undeniably given us a real sense of the future; but the point need not be labored, alas, that it has also given us a sense of doom. What is worse, for the first time it has put our overreaching fears for the future on a realistic basis.

What I think must be said here about the moral responsibility of science is at least this, that we cannot for very long succeed in shifting responsibility to one another. The scientist pleads that it is not he but the politician who is responsible for what is done with science. The politician in turn speaks of the moral bankruptcy of the members of the opposition party, or of foreign powers. Others of us point to the lack of leadership; and so it goes. But the responsibility must be accepted by all or it will be acknowledged by none; and accepted by each of us in his own way, as determined by the part played by each in the whole social process. A few decades ago, when, as now, there was much public concern about morality in government, the then Secretary of the Interior, the incomparable Harold Ickes, observed that no public official was ever known to have bribed himself. The level of morality in government corresponds to the moral level of the society at large. And just this is also to be said about science, not in order to exempt it from responsibility, but, on the contrary, to emphasize that we are all members of one body, sharing responsibility as we share in the benefits of its exercise. Neither the scientist nor what is called "the citizen" can look to the other as his savior and, simultaneously, as his sacrificial victim.

Now let me draw attention to two or three themes in the symposium concerning the ways of coping with the various problems that have been presented. There are a number of considerations having to do, not with the content of the moral judgments we are to make, but with the method by which we might reasonably expect to arrive at such judgments.

Throughout the discussions there has been general recognition, I think, of a point I would like to join in emphasizing, that moral judgments must be made empirically, at least as a necessary condition of their validity, if not also as a sufficient condition. Even if we suppose that moral judgments must be based on moral consensus, or that they derive from religious or metaphysical premises, we must recognize that facts are needed to give abstract principles a purchase on concrete action. We need facts, for example, to determine whether legalizing abortions might not increase the number of *illegal* ones rather than decrease them, or whether capital punishment might not increase the number of capital crimes rather than serve as a deterrent. If moral principles are to have concrete consequences, we must recognize, as I believe the participants in the symposium did recognize, that their content must change, and perhaps change markedly, as there are changes in the specifics of the concrete situations to which they are to apply.

Much American thought about moral issues—or at least, much of the public expression of such thought—seems to me to be not so much a matter of morality as of moralization: absolute, uncompromising, and somehow unreal. Conventional morality, I have said elsewhere, is a tyranny tempered by hypocrisy. We pretend that our moral standards embody eternal truths, and that our values remain always unchanged. In fact, we accommodate continually to the changing circumstances, individual and social, of moral action.

The fact is that moral problems—and especially those we have been dealing with here—are essentially and inescapably contextual in character. If only there were a definite set of rules in accord with which we could apply to these vexed questions the moral consensus of society! At times during the discussion one could almost hear a plea for such rules, a plea addressed I do not quite know to whom, though I am afraid that there was a hovering expectation that soon philosophy will enter the discussion and resolve the issues.

Nothing is further from my intentions, or my capabilities either, than to offer such rules. It is partly for just this reason that I have insisted that we must cope with these problems rather than espousing one or another purported solution for them. There is an inescapable need for—what shall I call it?— moral sensibility, or the exercise of good judgment, morally speaking. We must have some way of applying general principles to particular cases, and we cannot do that by rule. For if we had rules for the application of the general to the particular, we would still need sensibility and judgment to decide which rules to apply where. The generalities of law, of religion, of institutional policy all have their parts to play—not in providing antecedent solutions, however, but in so structuring concrete situations that coping with the contextual problems becomes possible.

A final feature of moral method was touched on by Dr. Beecher and others, but it did not receive the attention that I think it deserved. The moral judgment must accord with the principle of moral autonomy, as it has been known in philosophy since Immanuel Kant. The moral will must be a lawgiver unto itself, for even if we act, as moral agents, in obedience to laws laid down by others, we ourselves must accept the moral obligation the laws impose. But in that case, we are committed to respecting the moral autonomy of other moral agents as well. In opening the symposium Carleton Whitehead stated our concern as being fundamentally with the integrity of the individual. In Kant's formulation, morality rests on the categorical imperative that we ought never to treat a human being—whether the self or another—as a means only, and not also as an end-in-himself. The problems of the sanctity of life are problems not simply for the physician, but also, and jointly, problems for the patient, the patient's family, and perhaps his friends; they are problems not only for the researcher or experimenter, but also for his editor (as has been pointed out in the symposium), his publisher and his reviewers, his students and his professors, his administrators—in short, everyone caught up in that situation. We cannot make decisions for others; it is enough if we can decide for ourselves.

The last problem to which I turn concerns the basis for assigning to life so supreme a value. The word "sanctity" has, after all, a religious connotation, and while some in the symposium insisted that only religion can provide a basis for the sanctity of life, others took the position that in the modern world we must look elsewhere. It seems to me that our thinking about this problem, whatever the position taken, usually suffers from the parochialism of viewing all religion in the perspective of what we know it to have been in the history of the Western world, without regard to the great religions of Asia.

In Hinduism, for example, the sanctity of life is even more basic to morality than it is in the Judaeo-Christian tradition— in spite of the stereotype of Asian indifference to life. There has never been a Church Militant, for instance, in Hinduism, nor an Inquisition or Crusade. The ideal of *ahimsa* or nonviolence reaches out into every phase of life, even politics, where it is perhaps best known to us, in the form of *satyagraha* or passive resistance. Yet the moral principle is not grounded in religious faith but the other way around: in Hinduism, as also in Buddhism, morality is not derived from religion but is seen, rather, as prerequisite to religious experience.

In any case, what "sanctity" means in human experience is not determined by religious doctrine alone, but depends on how the doctrine is interpreted and applied to concrete situa-

165

tions. The Jain religion, to take another example, adheres more strictly to the principle of the sanctity of life than does any other religion known to me. A devout Jain scrupulously avoids knowingly destroying any animal life whatsoever. The empirical consequence of his principled action is that he protects, among other things, poisonous snakes, germ-laden rats, and vermin of all kinds. Because he refuses to cope with what I have called the paradox of life, the thrust of his action is not only to sanctify life but also often to degrade and even to destroy it.

Fortunately, for us to cope with the problems of the sanctity of life it is not necessary, I believe, to settle any questions of the relation between religious doctrine and moral practice. We can distinguish between the content of a morality, the concrete values contextually prized, and the ethical theory providing an explanation and justification for those values. Two people can share a morality and differ markedly in their ethics, or share an ethical theory and differ markedly in the morality they justify by it. The same policy might be defended by one man on utilitarian grounds and by another because it is the will of God, and different policies might be pursued if either utility or God's will is differently interpreted in a concrete situation.

If we approach the problems of the sanctity of life on a world-wide scale, as surely we must, I believe that it is of enormous importance to recognize that we do not need an operating consensus in ethical theory—religious, political, metaphysical, or whatever—but only an operating consensus in morality. We cannot say to other peoples, or to other groups in our own society, "Unless you share *my* faith I have no trust in our joint action to achieve shared values." To say that is to betray our own lack of faith.

I believe that we can all agree on the basic principle that Shils put before the symposium, that life is sanctified because for us, the living, it is the locus of all value. If life is not sacred, nothing else could be.

Let me conclude by telling you how the problem is dealt with in the Judiac tradition. The *Talmud* does not discuss the sanctity of life explicitly in general terms, but raises the question whether life is worth living, whether, that is, it might not have been better had man not been created at all. The school of Shammah held that it would indeed have been better, while the school of Hillel took the position that, though this might be true, since man *was* created, we have nothing to do but make the best of our lives. The discussion was lengthy, subtle, and involved; its import has been summarized in a classic folk witticism: "Of course it's better for man never to have been born at all—but not one Jew in ten thousand has such luck!"

For my part, I feel that it is we the living who are the lucky ones. At any rate, I feel lucky to have had the opportunity to share in these discussions with you. Thank you— and long life to you!